Burglar Alarm Systems

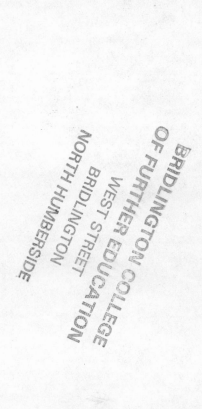

Other books by Vivian Capel:
Audio on Wheels
Master In-Car Entertainment
Radio Servicing Pocket Book, 3rd edn.

Burglar Alarm Systems

VIVIAN CAPEL

Newnes Technical Books

The Butterworth Group

United Kingdom   **Butterworth & Co (Publishers) Ltd**
London: 88 Kingsway, WC2B 6AB

Australia   **Butterworths Pty Ltd**
Sydney: 586 Pacific Highway, Chatswood, NSW 2067
Also at Melbourne, Brisbane, Adelaide and Perth

Canada   **Butterworth & Co (Canada) Ltd**
Toronto: 2265 Midland Avenue, Scarborough,
Ontario M1P 4S1

New Zealand   **Butterworths of New Zealand Ltd**
Wellington: T & W Young Building,
77–85 Customhouse Quay, 1, CPO Box 472

South Africa   **Butterworth & Co (South Africa) (Pty) Ltd**
Durban: 152–154 Gale Street

USA   **Butterworth (Publishers) Inc**
Boston: 10 Tower Office Park, Woburn, Mass. 01801

First published 1979 by Newnes Technical Books
a Butterworth imprint

© Butterworth & Co (Publishers) Ltd, 1979

British Library Cataloguing in Publication Data

Capel, Vivian
    Burglar alarm system.
    1. Burglar-alarms
    I. Title
    621.389'2   TH9739   78-40998

    ISBN 0 408 00405 3

Typeset by Butterworths Litho Preparation Department

Printed in England by Cox & Wyman Ltd,
London, Fakenham and Reading

Preface

Will your home or business figure in next year's crime statistics? With a break-in occurring every three minutes it is a distinct possibility. Even now your premises may be under observation by a thief awaiting the opportunity to enter your premises.

Along with good physical security, an alarm system is becoming an essential for every home and business. But which one to choose out of the many types and makes now on offer? What are their respective advantages, and which is most suitable for your premises? How can you plan a complete system, then install it? What are the points to watch out for and how can the pitfalls be avoided?

In this book we deal with the basic requirements and principles of an alarm system, and discuss in turn each one of its essential parts — control units, sensors, and sounding devices. The more exotic methods of intruder detection such as ultrasonic, infra-red and microwave detectors are described, with their particular features, as well as closed-circuit-television.

The planning of both the system and installation is well covered with plenty of practical hints and tips. Business premises get special attention in a chapter devoted to their particular security problems. Eight representative commercial systems are described and compared.

The information given in these pages will enable domestic or business occupiers to protect their premises from the unwelcome attentions of the burglar. There is also useful material which will be of interest to the professional installer and security officer. It is hoped the information presented will keep the intruder away from *your* door.

Vivian Capel

Contents

Introduction

WHAT PRICE SECURITY?

It is a sad comment on our present civilisation that one of our main boom 'industries' is that of crime. On average someone's home is broken into every three minutes. Apart from the material loss, which may to some extent be compensated for by insurance, the experience is a deeply traumatic one, the depression and feeling of insecurity can be long-lasting. Often the only cure is a move to another location with all the expense and upheaval which this entails. Even having once been a victim, there is no guarantee that the experience will not be repeated unless some positive steps are taken to prevent it.

As with road accidents there is a tendency for those who have not yet suffered to think, 'it won't happen to me', – if they think about it at all. No doubt the majority of victims have thought the same otherwise they would have gone to some trouble to make their homes more secure. You may think you have nothing worth stealing, but the thief does not know this and will find out if you give him half a chance. You may get a shock when you try to replace stolen items that you thought were not valuable. If the thief does not find anything, he make take his revenge by vandalism which can be very unpleasant. Remember that three-quarters of all break-ins are carried out by teenagers.

At one time home security systems were only fitted to the houses of wealthy persons to protect their many priceless possessions, but security is rapidly becoming an essential item for every home and business premises. Security of course, can only be relative, nothing can be absolutely thief-proof. Even bank vaults with their massive safes, and complex alarm systems have been burgled by a combination of planning, cunning, patience and sophisticated breaking equipment.

Each householder and business proprietor must therefore make up his mind as to the degree of security he feels appropriate to his circumstances. Maximum security in the home, for example, would mean steel bars across every window, steel linings to all outside doors, security locks every-where, concrete floors and impenetrable ceilings, together with a fool-proof alarm system. Obviously this would be inconvenient, undesirable and, in most cases, unnecessary. A combination of reasonable physical security and a good alarm system should give adequate protection.

Most house breakers, like car thieves, are out for a quick and easy job. Anything that looks a lot of trouble, especially if it is observed that an alarm is installed, will be strictly avoided. Why go to all the trouble and extra risk if there is a house down the road that is just begging to be broken into? (and most are). It is better to discourage entry than to thwart it because much damage can be done in the attempt. However, if the thief suspects that the house contains real valuables whether this is true or not, he may be prepared for extra trouble and risks. Any situation which may give rise to such a speculation would call for greater security.

Small business are vulnerable, especially where the premises are empty for many hours at a time. Businesses that carry expensive stock such as jewellers, furriers, wine and spirit merchants and tobacconists are at special risk. To this list can be added the chemist as drug addition has given special value to the stock. In most other cases the possibility of finding loose cash is a greater attraction than stealing stock. Although a quantity of cash may not be kept on the premises, the thief will not be aware of this, so security is still necessary to prevent entry and possible vandalism. The destruction of files and records could be a major set-back to any business, and this has often been done by disappointed intruders. A considerable choice of alarm systems now exists, ranging from elaborate and costly installations fitted by the makers or their agents to the cheaper d.i.y. outfits. Many questions therefore arise:

Is it best to let the experts do the job or can an effective installation be made by the home handyman?
Are the expensive systems worth the money and do the cheap ones pose a security risk?
How does an alarm system work and what features should be considered when choosing one?

A mistake could prove very expensive, so in this book we will deal with these and many other associated questions. We will describe what an alarm system should do, discuss practical problems and weigh up the merits of various types as applied to particular situations. Planning a system will be dealt with as well as installation. A chapter is also included on the special considerations arising in the protection of business premises. If applied and acted upon promptly, this information could mean that your home or business does *not* figure in the annual breaking-and-entering statistics!

1

Alarm System Requirements

The purpose of an alarm system is usually taken to be to alarm or inform others of the presence of an intruder, but really the best effect is to *alarm the intruder* before entry is effected. In other words, the obvious presence of an alarm system should act as a deterrent.

Should the intruder not be aware that a system is fitted then at least he will be scared off by the alarm sounding before stealing or doing any damage other than that of the forced entry. In many cases the alarm will sound at the first attempt and so the intruder will not actually set foot in the premises. To fulfill this purpose the alarm must therefore produce a loud, clear and insistent sound which will carry over a wide area. Large bells powered from the mains or heavy duty batteries are generally used, mounted in a position where the sound will travel far and not be masked. Small alarm devices operated by torch batteries cannot really achieve this requirement.

Reliability

Reliability is one of the most important factors. If the circuit should fail, it may do so just when it is needed; it only requires one failure at the wrong time to completely nullify the whole point of its existence.

The reliability of an alarm unit cannot easily be determined in advance, as it is only when installed and operating that any basic unreliability will show up. Any electronic component is capable of failure. BS 4200 and similar IEC standards in Europe define methods of expressing failure rates. These can be due to inherent weakness, normal or abnormal stresses during operation, and ageing. Failures can be sudden or gradual, partial or catastrophic (to quote the BS terminology); they can be predictable by previous examination or they can be unforeseen. An average failure rate for any component is arrived at by test procedures which predict the mean time to failure of a sample and the number of failures per thousand components.

This is not very reassuring when so much depends on it, and it proves that 100 % reliability cannot be guaranteed for any equipment employing electronic components. It is, of course, obvious that the fewer components there are, the greater the overall reliability, because each component constitutes a reliability hazard. Some alarm circuits fairly bristle with electronic components to give various desirable features and facilities, but each of these could add to the possibility of failure.

One circuit used no fewer than eight active semiconductor devices (transistors, integrated circuits and diodes), as well as many passive components such as resistors and capacitors. In contrast, another control circuit uses only two semiconductors; one of which would have little effect on the circuit if it failed and the other is active for only a fraction of a second to initiate the alarm.

The above examples do not necessarily indicate that any individual unit using a large number of components will frequently break down, while one with fewer parts will rarely if ever do so. It does mean that, statistically, the complex circuit is *more likely to* break down, and taking a batch of several thousand units, there will almost certainly be a higher incidence of faults than with the simpler device. This of course is assuming that the design parameters are such that the components are all operated within their specified ratings.

Another reliability factor is the choice of components; some types have proven much more reliable than others. For example, certain types of transistor have an excellent dependability record whilst others have a high failure rate. Some relay switches tarnish and produce a high resistance when not operated for a long period; others are gold-plated and tarnish-free.

False alarms

A system that gives false alarms is just as bad as one that breaks down completely, and they can be extremely inconvenient. To be awakened in the middle of the night by the alarm bell is not a pleasant experience, nor one that is likely to endear the householder to the neighbours. On business premises, the manager or key holder is likely to be hauled out of bed by the police to investigate, while if an alarm occurs during a holiday period, it may mean being summoned back from vacation. While the police investigate all reported alarms, they naturally take a dim view of too many false alarms on the same premises.

A system that is prone to give false alarms can also be a security hazard as it will tend to be ignored. One day it may be the real thing and nobody will take any notice. A trick used by some burglars is to deliberately set off the alarm, then wait nearby. The owner appears on the scene, assumes that a fault has caused a false alarm as there is no sign of a break-in, and not wishing to be disturbed again that night switches the system off intending to get it checked the next day. This, of course, is exactly what the thief hopes and when the commotion has abated, makes an entry without risk. The moral is, if the alarm un-accountably goes off, check for possible faults on the spot. If there are none, switch on the system again.

False alarms are usually caused by faulty wiring, careless securing of protected doors and windows, over-sensitive sensors, or actuation by non-human cause (pet animal, draughts, traffic vibration, etc). They are not often caused by the control unit, although this is not impossible.

Tamper-proofing

An alarm system is of little use if it can be easily deactivated by the intruder. As much as possible of the system should therefore be con-tained within the protected area so that it cannot be reached from the outside without actuating one of the alarm sensors. It should also be so designed that even if entry is made and the alarm set off, it could not be quickly silenced by the intruder. This means concealing vulnerable parts of the system such as the control unit, power supplies and bell wiring.

The bell itself is vulnerable and is often contained within a steel case. This, however, has other disadvantages. It reduces the volume of sound and may actually prove a hazard as the bell could be silenced by filling the case with plastic foam through the louvres. It is not so easy though to silence an open weatherproof bell with close-fitting dome. The best protection is to mount the bell high up in some inaccessable position. This also facilitates the distribution of sound over a wide area.

Wiring can be a security hazard and especially the wires from the bell. These need to be protected or concealed and, if possible, should pass through the outside wall directly into the bell without any exposed run. Failing this wires should be run in metal tubing. Inside the premises the bell wiring should be concealed as much as possible. Sometimes decoy wiring is employed to confuse and mislead a would-be tamperer.

Wiring to sensors is less vulnerable as tampering with this usually sets off the alarm, and special four-wire systems can be used to give extra security where premises may be open to the public and the possibility of tampering greater. Even so this wiring too should be run as un-obtrusively as possible. Practical methods of installing wiring are dealt with in chapter 12. Where there is a possibility of the bell wiring being tampered with, self-contained units which include the battery can be used. The wiring to the bell does not therefore supply power but is taken from the sensors or control unit, and any interference with it will cause the alarm to sound. This is also discussed later.

Cost of units

When so much is at stake, initial cost of installing an effective system is not usually a major consideration. However, it is natural to want to save money if this does not in any way reduce the degree of protection given.

There is quite a disparity in the costs of the various commercial units and the facilities which are offered. Most are sold as a kit including sensors, and some units have a greater number and variety of sensors than others. A number of types are only available from firms who install them, while others can be bought for d.i.y. installation. It can be seen, therefore, that there are many factors influencing the price, but there can also be other differences and the dearest is not necessarily the best. In fact in one case a lower priced kit is actually better than many of the higher cost brands. Some guidance is given in a later chapter as to what is currently available, but the information in this book should enable the reader to judge and evaluate any particular system for himself.

Running costs

One factor rarely considered is that of running costs. Most systems operate on the closed loop principle (see chapter 2); this requires a continuous circulating electric current when the system is on guard. In most cases current is supplied by the mains transformed down to a suitable low voltage. In the event of mains failure batteries are automatically switched in.

The actual current passed varies considerably from one make to another and this not only affects the running costs but also the reliability. For example, one make consumes 190 mA when on guard in the mains position which means a consumption of 45 W. Assuming the alarm is switched on every night when retiring, and for several hours on perhaps two evenings a week and also a period of three weeks vacation, this will give a total consumption of over 150 kWh or units of electricity each year — a not inconsiderable amount.

In the battery mode, the consumption is 60 mA for the same system. Should this be sustained for a lengthy period due to the blowing of a fuse or the mains being inadvertently switched off at the start of a holiday, it would prove a serious drain on the battery. Subsequently there may be insufficient power to sound and maintain the alarm (this requires a further 360 mA). In any case such a protracted period of battery operation would require a new battery in the interests of future security and as these now cost several pounds for a set, and costs are increasing, this would be an expensive item.

In contrast with this type, a number of units are designed to operate with a very low current. Values of a few millamperes are not uncommon and one model consumes just a tenth of a milliampere, six hundred times less than the above-mentioned system. This means that the mains can be dispensed with altogether and smaller cheaper batteries can be employed. The alarm can be left continuously on guard for a month or more and the batteries hardly notice the drain.

The elimination of the mains means simpler installation with no mains wiring or supply point. There is no transformer and other power supply circuitry, or automatic switch-over device; this makes for increased simplicity hence reliability, and also lower initial cost. Battery-only models should be operated only with a low-consumption bell.

Bells also vary in current consumption with different makes yet sound volume is not greatly affected for a particular-sized dome. A low-consumption unit will continue sounding for some considerable time before the battery polarises and requires to be rested, whereas a high-consumption model will soon polarise the battery and cease to function.

It follows from this that the loop current is an important parameter in any alarm system specification, and a system with a low value is to be preferred.

2

The Basic Alarm Circuit

There are four basic parts to an alarm circuit. First, there is the sounding device, usually a bell; second there is the power supply, which may be a battery or a mains supply. Next, there are the switches which are actuated by the intruder, often referred to as sensors, and finally a control which in its simplest form is just a master switch to switch the whole circuit on or off.

A simple alarm circuit

A simple circuit is shown in *Figure 2.1*. The master switch, bell and battery are connected in series, and several sensors in parallel are also connected in series with the bell and battery. These sensors may take the form of door switches that operate when a door is opened, or a pressure pad fitted under a carpet that closes the circuit when trodden on. Any number of sensors can be added to the circuit, and the bell will ring when any one of them is operated.

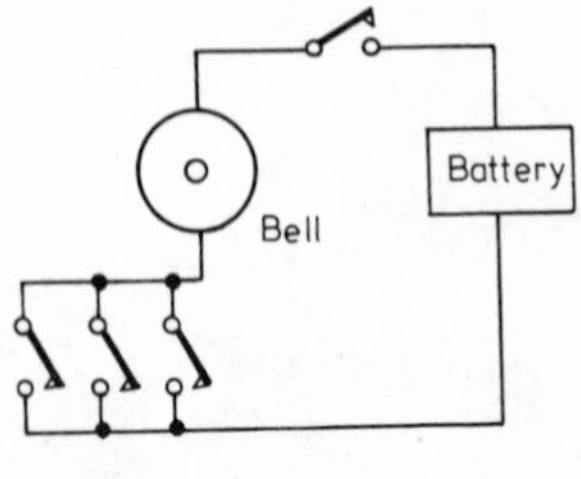

Figure 2.1 Basic alarm circuit consisting of bell, battery, control switch and parallel sensors

As it stands there is a very serious limitation to this circuit. If the bell rings when a door is opened, it can be stopped by simply shutting the door and thus opening the switch contacts. Alternatively, if the alarm is actuated by a pressure mat, it will stop as soon as the intruder steps off the mat. Obviously, such an arrangement is of little use as a security device.

What is required is a means whereby the alarm once started latches on and any subsequent alteration of the sensor conditions will have no effect at all on its continued sounding. Only switching off at the master switch will then silence it.

This latching facility is an essential part of any alarm system and usually consists of part of the control unit circuit, although it can also be contained in the bell housing. It can be accomplished mechanically

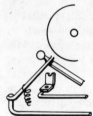

Figure 2.2 Simple mechanical latching system. The metal rod rests on bell striker and is pulled down to engage with metal contact by a spring when the striker moves. The rod and contact are connected across the sensor circuit and so keep the bell circuit closed

by means of an arm resting on the striker of the bell which, when the striker moves, slips off on to a contact cradle and is held on to it by a spring (*Figure 2.2*). The arm and the cradle form a switch which is connected across the sensor lines, and so the circuit is internally closed irrespective of whether the sensors are on or off. The arm is reset by means of a lever which lifts it off the cradle to rest again on the striker arm.

Similar arrangements were sometimes devised by d.i.y. alarm installers in the days when electrical relays were expensive, difficult to come by, and heavy on energising current. Now that suitable relays are readily available such methods are no longer needed.

Relays are commonly employed to latch the circuit in the 'on' position. These are switches that are actuated magnetically by a current flowing through a solenoid or coil of wire. When the current flows, a plunger is attracted to the iron core over which the coil is wound which becomes magnetized. This moves a pair of contacts which closes the circuit.

In *Figure 2.3* the coil of the relay is connected in series with the sensors so that if any one is actuated, current will pass through it. This closes a pair of switch contacts which not only completes the bell

Figure 2.3 Using a relay to latch the circuit on. When a sensor closes, current flows through the bell and the relay coil. The relay switch closes shorting the sensor circuit, so maintaining the alarm even if the original sensor is then opened

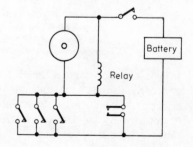

circuit but maintains current flowing through the relay coil thus keeping the switch closed irrespective of whether the original sensor circuit is now open or closed. The relay operates in a fraction of a second so there is no chance of an intruder reacting before it switches on and thereby defeating it.

Closed loops

The circuit shown in *Figure 2.3* is known as an 'open' circuit, that is, the sensor switches are normally in the open position, and when an intruder actuates one the switch closes. This arrangement has certain drawbacks. It is vulnerable to tampering as any person who has access to the protected premises when the alarm is switched off, i.e. a customer in business premises during business hours, may be able to cut one of the wires to one of the sensors. Thus that sensor would be neutralized, and the individual or an accomplice could then make an unauthorized visit at a later time without setting off the alarm.

Another snag is that the system is not easily tested. The wiring and contacts of a switch that is normally in the open position cannot be checked, except by closing it. Thus testing the circuit involves actuating each of the sensors in turn to see if they work and set off the alarm; this can obviously be time consuming and inconvenient. Even if a special test circuit is provided to avoid actually sounding the alarm, each sensor would still have to be operated individually.

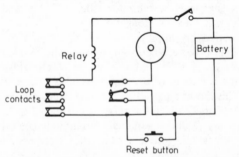

Figure 2.4 Relay latching circuit with closed loop. Coil is continuously energised holding the switch open. If a sensor opens, the relay is de-energised and the switch closes to sound the bell

A test of the system is therefore unlikely to be carried out very often and certainly not each time the alarm is set. A fault could develop, either caused deliberately by an intending intruder as mentioned earlier, or accidentally by damage to wiring or wear and tear on the switch, thus resulting in loss of protection.

An alternative which avoids these difficulties is the closed loop; this is shown in *Figure 2.4*. Instead of the sensors being normally open they are normally closed and are connected in series in a loop rather than being wired in parallel as in the open system.

If any of the sensors are actuated, the contacts are opened, thus open-circuiting the entire loop. This is interpreted by the control unit as an alarm condition which it does by passing a small current continually around the loop thereby holding off a relay, transistor, or other circuit device from operation. When the loop is broken the current ceases, the device switches over and the alarm sounds.

In the case of the simple relay circuit of *Figure 2.4*, the relay is continually energised by current passing through it and around the loop.

The relay has three contacts, one of which is common to the other two. When energised it closes with one and opens the other, and when de-energised the state is reversed. Opening the loop de-energises the relay, closing the contacts in series with the bell thereby switching it on. The contacts in series with the loop are opened thus latching the relay and preventing it switching back should the loop be re-closed. Closing the loop and pressing the reset button re-energises the relay and resets the circuit.

Advantages of the closed loop

It can be seen that the fact that the alarm does not sound when the circuit is switched on shows that the loop is continuous and current is passing around it. Therefore no part of the wiring has been cut or accidentally disconnected, neither are any of the sensor switch-contacts defective. Thus every sensor and all the wiring are in effect 'tested' at each switch-on. This assumption is based on the premise that the bell, power supply and control relays are operational. If a fault existed in any of these, obviously the alarm would not sound and the loop could also be defective.

It is not necessary to actuate each sensor in the circuit to find out if they are working, nor is it necessary to operate any sensor to test the alarm. This can be done by open-circuiting the loop by means of a switch connected in series with it at the control box. Thus if the alarm does *not* sound when the system is switched on, but *does* when the series test button is pressed, the loop and all parts of the circuit including battery and bell are shown to be in order.

If any part of the loop wiring or its sensors have been tampered with by disconnection or wire cutting, this will be immediately obvious as soon as the system is switched on because the alarm will sound.

A closed loop system has a much higher security rating than the open type of circuit, and it is far easier to test. The main drawback is that it consumes current all the time it is switched on. With many systems this means that power is derived from the mains supply necessitating mains wiring and an automatic switch-over to batteries in the event of mains failure. All this adds to complication and cost. Even when mains powered, the running costs can be high as was shown in chapter 1. Some systems are designed to pass a very small loop current which eliminates the necessity of using mains for power, and furthermore, instead of draining the battery, actually lengthens its life.

The closed loop is therefore the preferred arrangement and normally used in most alarm systems. Some sensors, such as pressure mats, are only made in the mode that completes the circuit when actuated, that is, they are normally open. Systems which use these have two separate circuits, a closed loop for the main sensors, and an open type of circuit for the pressure mats and similar devices.

In such installations only the closed loop can be tested at the control box; mats must be checked by individual operation. As they are usually supplementary to the main system of sensors, a fault on any one would not constitute a major security hazard. An intruder would almost certainly actuate a main sensor even if he was not 'caught' by a pressure mat. These then can be tested at less frequent intervals.

Four-wire systems

For the majority of applications, especially in the home, the closed loop supplemented by one or two pressure mats gives a high degree of security. For business premises where visitors are admitted freely and where valuable goods are stored, it may not be sufficient.

A loop system can be defeated by short-circuiting part or all of the loop. Thus if a pair of wires is observed going to a protected means of access such as a door or window, the intending intruder may scrape a small area of insulation away from both wires adjacent to each other and either twist the exposed parts together or wrap a piece of wire around them. A pair of wires running in the vicinity of the control box would very likely serve a number of sensors, a major part of or even the entire loop, and bridging these could put most, if not all, of the system out of action. Normal testing procedure would not reveal anything amiss as current would circulate through the bridge.

If the wiring is inconspicuous and as inaccessible as possible, bridging will be difficult, certainly more difficult than just snipping a wire which will incapacitate an open-type circuit. A suitable bridging point must be found, and insulation from both wires be removed without damaging the wire. This takes time and a steady hand and there is always the risk of being discovered in the act. Even so this is possible, especially in large premises where not all the staff may be known to each other, and there are strangers coming and going. The intending burglars may pose as workers or electricians doing repair or maintenance work and would very likely not be questioned.

So although offering good tamperproof security, the single closed loop is not infallible in certain situations. For this reason a four-wire circuit is sometimes used. With this, the sensors have two pairs of contacts, one pair are normally open and the other normally closed. When actuated, the open pair closes and the closed pair opens. These are used with control boxes that have both open and closed loop facilities, the closed contacts are connected up with all the other sensors in a loop in the normal way, while the open contacts are wired in parallel to the open terminals of the control box.

Each unit is therefore two sensors in one. For a start this doubles the security as if one sensor suffers from failure or tampering, the other will operate. Both sensors are not needed to trigger the alarm; either will do so without the other. The main advantage of the four-wire system is the dilemma it presents to a would-be tamperer. To successfully defeat it the intruder must bridge the wires going to the closed contacts and also cut one of the wires going to the open contacts. The difficulty is identifying the wires; if the wrong two are bridged the alarm will sound when the system is switched on. There are six possible ways of bridging two out of four wires and only one is correct. In addition one wire out of the four must be cut and two of these would sound the alarm if broken.

There is no means of identifying the wires as there is no standard colour coding — this would defeat its purpose. In fact, the colours of the wires are usually changed along their length so a red wire at one end may wind up green at the other. Thus it is practically impossible to tamper with a four-wire system and defeat it with certainty, without inside knowledge of the particular wiring.

These are the basic elements of alarm circuits that are included in most alarm systems. They are standard features which will be encountered in the maker's literature and specifications. There are numerous other facilities and refinements which will be described later on.

3

The Control Unit

The control unit is the heart of the whole alarm system. Other parts of the installation, the bell, sensors and supply, vary little and conform to a generally standard design. It is the control unit that determines the flexibility, the facilities available and to some extent the reliability of the system. Its first function is to provide circuit latching so the alarm continues to sound having been triggered off by the sensor. To do this the majority of control circuits use relays as described in the last chapter but these present a problem when used in conjunction with a closed loop.

If we again look at the circuit shown in *Figure 2.4* it will be seen that the relay is energised all the time the alarm is on guard. This holds the contacts open, and when the loop is broken, the relay is de-energised and the contacts close so completing the bell circuit. Now relay coils are designed to operate over a certain voltage range which is centred on a fixed nominal value. A 12 V relay for example may operate over a range of 8-17 V. Relays are available in many different voltage ratings from 6 V up to mains voltage of 240 V, but as a certain minimum power is required to move the plunger or rocker; it follows that for the lower voltage ratings, the current must be higher. (Power is the product of voltage and current.)

A sensitive modern relay requires around 1 W to operate decisively, it will move with a smaller current but with less certainty. Many relays take much more than 1 W, but it can be calculated that a 1 W relay operating at 12 V, which is the standard voltage of most smaller systems, will take

$$\frac{1 \text{ watt}}{12 \text{ volts}} = 0.083 \text{ amps}$$

or 83 mA.

With a closed loop, a current of this order must be passing continuously to keep the relay energised and would constitute a heavy drain on any battery. A mains-derived supply would therefore be essential.

Thyristor trigger circuits

As an alternative to the relay it is natural to look to the field of semi-conductors (transistors) for a latching device that will take very little current in the on-guard position. One type which appears ideal for the task is the thyristor (the silicon-controlled rectifier). This is a combination of semi-conductor elements arranged to behave like two integrated transistors. It has three connections, an anode, a cathode and a gate. If the gate is shorted to the cathode, the device will not conduct, but when a positive voltage is applied to the gate, the thyristor will conduct heavily.

The feature of the device is that if the positive gate voltage is now removed, it will continue to conduct until the current is switched off. So the positive pulse at the gate triggers the thyristor into conduction after which the gate plays no further part in the operation.

Theoretically, the thyristor seems ideally suited for triggering and latching alarm circuits. A basic circuit using a thyristor is shown in *Figure 3.1*. The device is connected in series with the bell and the supply voltage. The gate is connected to the positive of the supply through a high value resistor, and the loop is connected between the gate and the cathode. Thus the gate is effectively short-circuited to the cathode via the loop and so the thyristor does not conduct and the bell receives no current.

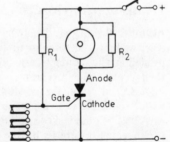

Figure 3.1 Simple thyristor circuit. The gate is shorted to the cathode through the loop. When the loop is opened a positive voltage through R_1 makes the thyristor conduct which it continues to do until switched off. R_2 maintains a small current through the thyristor when the trembler in the bell breaks contact

When the loop is broken by the actuation of a sensor, the gate is no longer tied down to the cathode and a positive voltage through the resistor appears on it. This makes the device conduct and the bell rings. Any subsequent change in the voltage on the gate caused by re-forming the loop has no effect and the bell continues to ring until the power is switched off. A resistor is shunted across the bell to maintain current through the thyristor when the bell trembler contacts are open otherwise the thyristor would switch off.

In the guard position, current flows along the loop through the resistor, but as this is of a high value (thousands of ohms) the current is small, just a milliamp or so. Thus economy is achieved with a simple latching circuit without even any switch contacts to deteriorate.

While this application is excellent in theory, in practice thyristors have not yet established such a good record of reliability as relays. This is unfortunate as otherwise the thyristor seems well suited for the job.

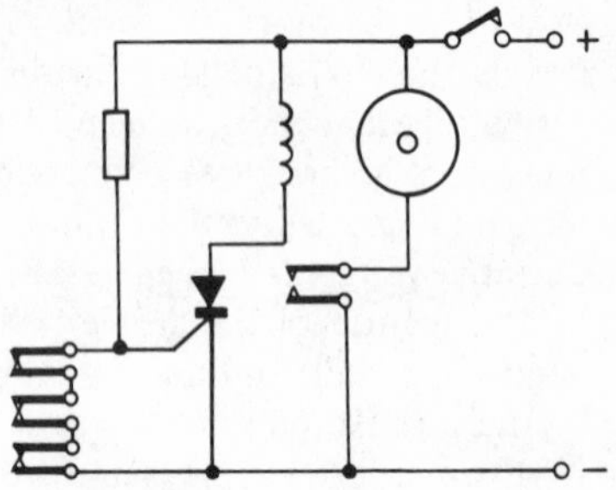

Figure 3.2 Using a relay with the thyristor to avoid passing bell current through the thyristor

Another fact is that the bell current passes through the thyristor all the time it is sounding. This current is high (several hundred milliamps) and very spiky in waveform, which are just the conditions likely to cause the component's early demise. A thyristor could be used in conjunction with a relay (*Figure 3.2*), but then its advantage of contact-less latching would be lost.

Transistor relay circuits

Although the magnetic relay has the drawback of taking a heavy current, it is a well-proven component with excellent reliability. This is, of course, providing the contacts are non-tarnishing, are operated well within their current-carrying rating, and that the relay is enclosed to inhibit ingress of atmospheric moisture. The relay can be used in conjunction with a transistor to give a reliable latching circuit with low loop current.

A basic circuit is shown in *Figure 3.3*. The transistor, like the thyristor, is connected in series with the load, which in this case is the relay coil and not the bell. A high-value resistor is connected between the base of the transistor to the positive supply, and the loop is connected between base and emitter. The circuit is similar to that using the thyristor. When the loop is open-circuited, positive forward bias is applied to the base of the transistor which causes it to conduct, thereby energising the relay.

There are two pairs of switch contacts, one shorts the transistor from collector to emitter, and this effectively connects the relay coil directly across the supply. It is thereby energised independently of the transistor and thus latches on. It cannot be de-energised other than by switching off the supply.

A feature of this arrangement is that the transistor only triggers the alarm, its continuation is not dependent on it. Furthermore as the transistor is then shorted out, its emitter/collector junction cannot be damaged by spiky waveform generated by the bell. Only the relay energising current passes through the transistor, and not the bell current, even for starting purposes.

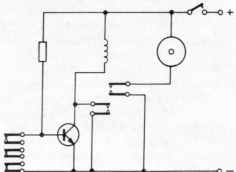

Figure 3.3 Transistor relay circuit. Two sets of contacts are needed in the relay, one to switch the bell on and the other to latch the relay on. If the bell and relay coil were in parallel only one contact pair would be needed but the bell current would pass through the transistor

Figure 3.4 To avoid possible damage to the transistor from voltage spike generated in the relay coil, a diode can be connected across the coil

The circuit has therefore built-in reliability and, in addition, a transistor can be chosen with a good reliability record. The second pair of contacts are used to switch the bell, so the bell circuit is quite separate and, if desired, could be supplied from another power source.

Current passed through the transistor must be sufficient to energise the relay and, as there will be some voltage drop across the transistor which will be subtracted from the supply voltage, the operating voltage of the relay must be sufficiently low to come within the available range.

If, for example, there is a 2 V drop across the transistor when it is conducting and the supply is a 12 V battery, this leaves 10 V to operate the relay. Allowance must be made for the battery ageing and losing voltage, say another 2 V. Thus the relay should be capable of operating at 8 V. A nominal 12 V relay should therefore be chosen that will operate well below 8 V. A good design will take this into account because although the batteries should not be allowed to deteriorate too far before being replaced, there will be a loss of voltage during their useful life.

The higher the current passed by the transistor, the lower will be the voltage drop across it and the more positive the relay action. Transistor collector current depends on two factors, the base current and the *hfe* (transistor current gain). So to achieve a high current, the chosen transistor should have a high gain consistent with good reliability, and sufficient base current. Collector current is in fact base current multiplied by the *hfe*. The base current in turn is controlled by the base resistor;

it must be low enough in value to give adequate base current when the loop is opened, yet high enough to give a moderately low current through the loop which is desirable in the interests of battery economy.

The actual value depends on the type of transistor used and its *hfe*, and also the current requirement of the relay with a safety margin for falling battery voltage. Careful design and choice of components enables quite a high value to be employed with corresponding low loop current. One control unit using this type of circuit has achieved a loop current of only a tenth of a milliamp.

These then are the three basic types of latching control circuits: relay, thyristor, and transistor/relay, but there are variations and elaborations. Additional semi-conductor devices such as transistors, operational amplifiers, and logic gates are sometimes used to give various facilities, but over-complex circuits can mean a reduction in reliability.

Certain circuit refinements are desirable. The inductive pulse generated when the energising current through the relay ceases, could damage the transistor, so a protection diode across the relay coil can be included to bypass such pulses.

Under certain conditions the external loop can cause the transistor to oscillate, generating a negative base voltage which cuts off the collector current and paralyses its operation. It is also possible that the loop can pick up strong radio transmissions which could trigger the alarm. Low-current loop systems are more likely to do this than others because they are more sensitive.

Both conditions can be prevented by the inclusion of r.f. bypass and filter components in the transistor input circuit and these should be included in any good design. As such components are precautionary rather than essential for the normal functioning of the alarm, their inclusion poses no reliability hazard.

Testing facilities

Some means of testing the system is essential if any faults or tampering are to be quickly detected and not constitute a security risk. While most control units have built-in test facilities, they vary in their extent and usefulness.

The simplest form is a push-button which open-circuits the loop. The circuit is thus activated and the alarm set off. While this is the most certain form of test, it is neither convenient nor desirable.

As frequent testing is recommended, (for maximum security this should be each time the system is switched on) the bell will be frequently heard. This, in time, will have the same effect as frequent false alarms, neighbours will get accustomed to it and so may ignore it if there should ever be a real break-in. Also if the alarm is switched on every time the householder goes out for any period, it will tell the neighbourhood, and although the premises may be protected by the alarm, it is best not to advertise one's absence. A further snag is when switching on at night before retiring; neighbours will not be very happy with a nightly burst of alarm bell, especially if you are a late bird!

Clearly then, testing by actually sounding the alarm is not really practicable each time the system is switched on, except perhaps periodically, say once a month. This will not only completely test the system, but will let it be known in the neighbourhood that a working alarm system is installed, not just a dummy bell-box to deter would-be intruders. To prevent anyone mistaking such tests for the real thing, they could be carried out at the same time of day on each occasion, and with plenty of evidence that you are at home, (windows open, car outside, etc.)

The normal routine testing though will have to be silent. The test employed in some control units is to connect the loop to an indicator lamp when the control switch is in the 'test' position. If it lights up, the loop is continuous and the alarm can be switched on. If it fails to light the loop must be open, due either to a fault in the wiring or more likely because a door or window has been left open. If the alarm was switched on, in this condition it would start to sound. So, testing the loop before switching on prevents false alarms and is a check that all wired doors and windows are closed.

While loop wiring or careless closures are the most common causes of faults, the possibility of a latching circuit malfunction cannot be ruled out and this would not be revealed by such a test. In another type of test, an indicator lamp is switched in place of the bell. If the lamp comes on when switched to 'test', it means that the circuit has been triggered by an open-circuit loop so, in this case, the lamp should NOT light. If it does not, the loop is continuous and a test can then be made of the control circuit. This is done by pressing a button which open-circuits the loop. The lamp should immediately light and stay alight when the button is released, showing that the latching circuit is working. Some units have a buzzer instead of a light.

Both types of test are used, but the second is preferable because it tests more of the circuit. The types can be easily distinguished: with the first, the light comes *on* if the loop is intact, with the second it stays *off*. With the latter, a further operation (usually pressing a button) is needed to bring the light on, thus testing the control circuit.

Even with the second test an important and vulnerable part of the system remains unchecked, that is the bell and its wiring. The bell trembler contacts could become oxidized producing a high resistance, and although the bell may be inaccessible and so unlikely to be damaged or tampered with, the wiring especially at the control box end could become damaged or disconnected. Such troubles would show up at the next alarm-sounding test but could leave the system inoperative for a spell before it was due. Thus the premises could be unprotected for an unknown period of time.

Such risks are greatly reduced by the test used in one make of control box. A small, carefully controlled current is passed through the bell circuit. This flows through the bell but is too small to sound it. Testing procedure is the same as for the second type of test, and so involves no further complication for the user. When the light comes on in response to the test button, every part of the system (except pressure mats), loop, control and latching circuit, and the bell is shown to be in order. The lamp will not light if the bell circuit is disconnected. This obviously is the most comprehensive testing method, apart from actually sounding the alarm, and has much to commend it.

Indicator lamps

On large installations, facilities are commonly provided to identify the location of the disturbed sensor. It is evident that in a factory or large office block, finding an intruder or his point of entry could be a 'needle-in-the-haystack' task in the event of the alarm sounding. A number of separate loops, usually one per floor or floor area unit, are used each with its own input relay. The relays have an extra pair of contacts which supply an indicator lamp, so there is a lamp for each loop which comes on when that loop is disturbed. The search is thus considerably narrowed.

With all these indications, there is a possibility of the operator being misled due to the indicator lamp going open-circuit. Ordinary filament lamps have a limited life and sooner or later will expire. This could happen at a critical time, or lead to much inconvenience as trying to trace a non-existent fault. For this reason, some control units are fitted with LED (light-emitting-diodes) indicators. These diodes have no filaments but are made of semiconducting material that emits light when an electrical current is passed through it. In theory these should never fail, and in practice they are far more reliable than a filament lamp. They do not emit a lot of light, not as much as a lamp, but it is enough for a test indicator.

Most mains/battery control units have a pilot light to show when the mains is switched on and the unit is in the on-guard mode. Whether or not this is necessary or even desirable is a debatable point. When the control box is in a conspicuous place it does serve as a reminder that the system is switched on or off. Such a position though, is not a good one from the standpoint of security. An intruder may attempt to silence the alarm by attacking the control unit if it is readily visible, and in a darkened hall, a glowing light will lead him right to it. The best solution is to hide the control box if at all possible, and certainly not draw attention to it. Hence a pilot light is of dubious worth and, in any case, if the box is hidden no-one would see the light.

The control circuit is usually housed in a metal box; some boxes have a tamper-proof lid which operates by means of a small microswitch inside the unit. When the lid is removed, the switch is released and the alarm triggered. The main idea behind this is to discover any daytime tampering with the system in business premises.

Business alarms often have a 'day' position as well as the normal on-guard or night position. With this, the usual sensors are not in circuit, as obviously people are coming and going through protected doors and walking on pressure mats. Extra leads are often included in the sensor wiring which are active in the 'day' position, thus any attempt to interfere with them will set off the alarm. This 'day' circuit is also known as the 'tamper' circuit, and the microswitch under the control box lid is wired to it. Sometimes a similar circuit is provided in the bell box, but this is usually connected to its own latching circuit and battery power supply where maximum security is required.

Key control switches

The majority of control units use a key to switch on or off and thus prevent an intruder from switching the alarm off. Two keys are usually provided. Although apparently increasing security, there are grounds for questioning this practice especially for home systems. It is easy for an intruder to silence the system by wrenching the box off the wall and cutting the bell wires. The use of a key to switch off therefore seems rather pointless; the jemmy is a most effective 'key' that will deal with all boxes! It is far better to conceal the control unit and it is unlikely the intruder will search for it with the alarm sounding, but if it is visible he may well try to stop it by force.

If a householder has taken precautions and fitted locks to all doors and windows, he will already have a ring bristling with keys. An extra unnecessary key will not usually be viewed with favour, to say nothing of the inconvenience of having to use it every time the system is switched on or off. In the case of large business systems the installation is secured with heavy fixings which would take much time and effort to successfully attack. Furthermore it may be possible for unauthorised persons to gain access to the control unit to switch it off. For example, an intruder may hide on the premises during business hours and break *out* afterward. If he could just switch off the alarm, his task would be relatively easy and would pass undetected until the next morning. For such installations, key switches are essential to maintain security.

Panic buttons

A very useful extra facility provided by some alarm control units is provision for wiring a panic button. This is a push-button positioned

near the front or back door, or upstairs in the bedroom. If desired several
can be fitted, in different places. The purpose is to sound the alarm in
case of personal attack by someone forcing their way into the house.
Where a woman is alone in a house for any length of time this can add
greatly to her peace of mind even if, as it would be hoped, it is never
used. If the necessity of use did arise, then it could mean the difference
between comparative safety and great personal danger and injury.

One of the main factors with a panic button is that it must be ready at
all times, even when the alarm system is switched off, and this is where the
technical problems arise. The success in solving these determines the value
of the facility. Clearly the switch must be bypassed, but as the latching

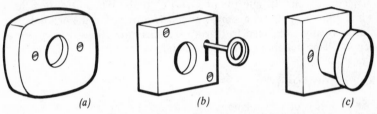

*Figure 3.5 Panic emergency buttons. (a) Surface mounting unit with recessed
button. (b) Recessed button with key reset. (c) Large profile button. (a) and (c)
press on and press off*

circuit is switched off, many panic buttons are just connected in series
with the bell and battery. This means that the button must be kept
depressed for the alarm to continue sounding. Obviously anyone being
attacked is unlikely to be able to keep their finger on a button!

More usually the button has a mechanical latch, pressing it once
completes the circuit and pressing it the second time releases it. The
action is like some reading lamp switches that you press-for-on then
press-for-off. This is an improvement over the straight bell-push type of
button, as the pressure does not have to be maintained, but even these
types have their drawbacks. If the intruder knows about panic buttons
and how they work he can operate it himself and silence the alarm.

To prevent this possibility there is the key-release button. The button
is pressed to sound the alarm, but it can only be released by using a key.
These are often used in the form of foot-operated switches under the
counter in banks, post-offices and jewellers where a hold-up is a
possibility.

The security of these buttons depends on how they are fixed and
wired. If, as is likely in the home, there is exposed wiring over the surface of the wall, the security is low. The device is not part of a loop but
is an open-circuit switch, which means that if the wiring is cut the alarm
will stop. A quick slash from a knife could do this all too quickly.

Ideally, the button should trigger a latching circuit in the control unit just like the normal sensors, then once it is pressed there is no way of silencing the alarm other than from the control box. This, however, adds to the number of components and complexity of the control circuit, hence the cost; it also complicates the switching. As the panic button must work even when the control unit is switched off, how then do you switch the panic circuit off? One solution is to have another switch which must be left on and only turned off to silence the panic circuit, or a 'day' position on the main control, in which the panic button would be alive and could be silenced by turning the control to the true 'off' position. However, bearing in mind human fallibility, there is always the possibility that the switch would be turned off at the control leaving the panic button inactive, perhaps at the very time it may be needed.

Clearly, the problems associated with the panic circuit are not easily solved, although one maker has done so quite neatly. The sensor loop operates a transistor relay, the transistor being switched out when the system is off. The relay remains in circuit, hence is ready to be triggered by the panic button, but because it is operated in the open-circuit mode, it draws no current unless actually energised by the button. Other open-circuit devices such as pressure mats also actuate the relay directly, not going through the transistor, but they are routed through one pole of the control switch and so are switched off with the rest of the system.

The main function switch is not key operated, but additional security is given by an unmarked cancel-button which must be depressed at the same time the switch is turned to 'off' to stop the alarm. To silence the alarm after activation by the panic button, only the cancel button need be depressed, the switch being already in the 'off' position. Thus a maximum security panic-button facility is given with no extra complication of the circuit or controls. Ordinary bell pushes can be used for the buttons, and any number can be fitted. This incidentally is the same model that has the lowest loop current and gives total test facilities including the bell circuit (see chapter 14).

A facility offered by many control units is a time delay that enables the user to make an exit from the protected area without setting off the alarm. Usually there is a separate circuit for the delayed door sensor, the others being active immediately the system is switched on. There are variations between models, with some the delay starts from the moment of switching on so the user must make his exit within a specified time, while with others the delay starts from the time the exit door is opened, giving a few seconds to get through it. These and other exit arrangements are discussed more fully in chapter 8.

4

Power Supplies

Most alarm systems are powered from the mains supply. This is essential in the case of simple relay circuits because the relay energising current is drawn continuously through the closed loop and can be anything from 20 mA to 80 mA; a dry battery subject to a drain of this order would soon be exhausted. Although bells are available that will work directly off the mains they are not used in normal alarm circuits. If they were, there could be no battery standby facility in the event of the mains supply failing. Furthermore if the latching relay also operated at mains voltage, the sensor wiring would be at mains potential and highly dangerous in view of the thin wiring and insulation generally used.

The operating voltage for domestic and small business alarm systems is 12 V, higher voltages being sometimes used in larger industrial systems. As power is the product of voltage and current, a low-voltage circuit requires higher current to achieve a given bell power. The higher the current, the greater the voltage drop hence power loss — due to the resistance of the connecting wires. So a low voltage circuit will lose more volts than a high voltage one. As the voltage was low to start with, the proportion lost will be even greater. Hence 6 V, although readily and more cheaply obtainable from a battery, is rather low to give adequate power for an alarm bell. Where long cable runs are necessary, such as in factory installations, 24 V may be required but, normally 12 V is perfectly suitable for the majority of smaller systems.

To operate from the mains, a transformer is needed to step down the voltage. This transformer is similar to the familiar door-bell type, but is more generously proportioned to handle the higher power. Bells described as d.c. models will work off a.c. as well, and so the alarm bell will function from either the transformer or the standby battery. A.c. bells on the other hand work off a.c. only, because they lack the trembler mechanism of the d.c. versions.

Change-over relay

If the mains supply fails provision must be made for the system to automatically switch over to the standby battery. This is usually done by means of another relay. The energising coil is connected directly across the mains input which means that as long as mains voltage is present the relay is energised, see *Figure 4.1*. (A relay will operate with either a.c.

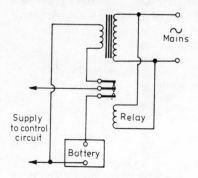

Figure 4.1 Battery/mains changeover circuit. The relay coil is energised from the mains thus keeping the circuit switched to the transformer secondary. If the mains fail the relay is de-energised and the contacts switch in the battery

or d.c. supplies). In this position, the relay contacts switch the alarm circuit to the secondary winding of the mains transformer and so it derives its power from the mains.

If the mains voltage disappears, the relay is no longer energised and it switches over to its 'at rest' contacts. These connect the circuit to the battery which thereby takes over supplying the circuit. When the mains supply is restored, the relay is again energised and the system switches back automatically to mains operation.

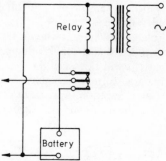

Figure 4.2 An alternative changeover circuit. The relay is supplied from the transformer secondary, thus it will switch in the battery if the transformer should fail

There is a reliability risk with this circuit. A transformer winding could go open-circuit which would deprive the system of its supply, yet because the mains voltage is present at the input, the relay would not switch over. An alternative arrangement is to use a low-voltage relay connected across the secondary of the transformer (*Figure 4.2*).

The relay receives its energising current from the transformer, so if this develops a fault, the relay will switch over to the battery. The drawback is that the transformer must supply current for the changeover relay and the latching relay continuously and so must be rated to provide this for long periods without overheating.

Although the combined current is not excessive for a transformer, there is little or no ventilation in the control box and there could be a significant temperature rise. It may be noted that there is a close relation between failure in electronic components and temperature increase.

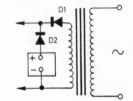

Figure 4.3 A simple yet very effective changeover circuit using two diodes, which isolate the transformer and battery from each other. Voltage output from the transformer must be slightly higher than the battery voltage

There is another method of switching over which eliminates the use of a relay entirely. This is by using a pair of diodes as switches, the circuit being shown in *Figure 4.3*. In this case, the supply from the transformer must be a little higher, say 1 V more than the battery.

When operating from the mains, current flows from the transformer through D1 to the alarm circuit. The current is therefore rectified to direct current but this is incidental to the operation of the circuit. Current cannot flow into the battery because the rectifier in series with it, D2 prevents it passing in that direction. As the voltage from the transformer is higher than the battery voltage, D2 is reverse biased which means it does not pass current in the forward direction. Thus the battery is isolated and current will not flow from it into the alarm circuit.

If the mains supply disappears, D2 is no longer reverse biased and current will flow into the external circuit. It will not pass back through the transformer secondary because it is prevented by D1. Unlike the relay changeover, this circuit does not take extra current when operating from the mains and also a pair of diodes are less costly than a relay.

The dry battery

Dry batteries are based in principle on the Leclanche cell (*Figure 4.4*). In its simplest form the cell employs a zinc negative electrode and a carbon positive, immersed in a solution of ammonium chloride known commonly as sal-ammoniac. A potential difference of about 1.5 V is produced by the chemical action which eats away the zinc and also liberates bubbles of hydrogen gas. These bubbles form around the carbon and effectively insulate it by preventing contact with the solution; thus the action of the cell is paralysed. The cell is then said to be *polarised* and it must be rested to allow the gas to clear away before it can be used again. The higher the current taken from the cell, the more gas is generated and the quicker it will polarise.

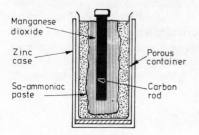

Manganese dioxide

Zinc case

Sa-ammoniac paste

Porous container

Carbon rod

Figure 4.4 The Leclanché cell which is the basis for most modern battery cells

This is one of the main problems with this type of cell as it restricts the amount of continuous current it can give out. The effect is minimised by introducing a chemical such as manganese dioxide as a depolarising agent. This has a strong affinity for hydrogen and the reaction is for one of its oxygen atoms to combine with a pair of hydrogen atoms to form a molecule of water leaving manganese oxide behind. Thus the hydrogen is removed and the only adverse effect is a slight dilution of the electrolyte by the chemically produced water.

This reaction takes time, and it is still possible if the current exceeds a certain level for the cell to become polarised by hydrogen being liberated faster than the depolariser can handle it. So, the discharge current and the effectiveness of the depolariser sets a limit on the length of time a cell can be used before resting.

In the modern dry cell, the negative zinc electrode is formed into a cylindrical case. A carbon rod is packed around with depolariser which is immersed in a sal-ammoniac paste contained in a porous container. This is inserted in the zinc case which is surrounded by a further steel case to prevent corrosion from exhausted batteries damaging equipment.

Irrespective of the size of the cell, the voltage remains the same, but the current capacity varies. Large cells are therefore needed for high current applications. Batteries that give a higher voltage are made up of a number of cells connected in series (strictly speaking a 'battery' is more than one cell). The 6 V lantern battery comprises four cells and the HP 1 is made up of eight cells.

The normal cell is quite adequate for long small discharges or short heavy ones, but if a heavy discharge is to be sustained, it will polarise and a 'high-power' version should be used. The chemical formula and construction of these is slightly different, very thin paper separators are used and, in particular, a larger quantity of high-grade manganese depolariser. This gives fast depolarising and so allows for higher maximum continuous currents.

An interesting feature with all dry-cell types of battery is that a small occasional discharge keeps the cell in good condition and it will last considerably longer than a battery that is not used at all. This is of particular interest in the case of alarm systems having low loop currents. Batteries used to power these are working in almost ideal conditions and should last for a considerable period, often a matter of years. Their life will also depend on the number of times that the bell has been sounded and for how long. Unless there has been an actual alarm, bell sounding will be only a matter of a few seconds a month for testing and should take little out of the battery.

Alarm batteries

In assessing the suitability of a battery for powering an alarm it is necessary to analyse the requirements of the circuit and operating conditions. In the case of a mains battery system with a high loop current, mains failure may mean that the battery could be called upon to produce the high loop current for some period, and then have a reserve of power to sound the bell if required. A high-power unit such as the 12 V HP1 would obviously be needed but a cheaper alternative is a pair of 6 V batteries which have screw terminals and so can conveniently be connected in series.

In the case of low loop-current battery systems, the normal running current plus occasional bell tests hardly warrant the use of a high-power battery. Should a break-in occur, providing the bell is of moderate consumption, an ordinary large capacity battery, such as a pair of lantern units, should sustain the bell for at least half-an-hour, before polarising. This should be more than enough to scare off the intruders and attract outside attention.

There is here an element of built-in battery economy. When a low power battery polarises, the current is very small and so it ceases to run down. After a short period of rest it should be ready to give further service. A high-power battery on the other hand will keep supplying current until it *is* run down and so would have to be replaced. No doubt someone would arrive on the scene to switch it off before that happened, but it does show that the high-power battery is not essential, providing loop current is low.

The lantern battery is ideal for a unit having a low loop current and is used in at least one make of alarm. It has the advantage of being cheaper than the HP1, and is widely available, which could be useful in an emergency.

Eventually the battery must be replaced, and in the interests of security this would be before it was actually exhausted. A voltage test with a voltmeter is not a particularly good indication unless it is measured while current is being drawn through a load such as a 6 V bulb as used in lantern torches if it is a lantern battery, or a 12 V lamp for the high-power type. If the battery reads below 5 V for the 6 V unit or 10 V for the 12 V unit, it should be discarded. Failing a voltmeter test, check the brightness of the indicator lamp, if it is dim compared to its original state, a replacement battery is required.

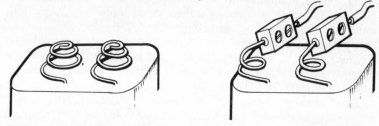

Figure 4.5 (left) Spring terminals as fitted to the PJ 996 lantern batteries. (right) Connections can be made by uncoiling the ends and fitting terminal screw connectors

This may seem rather wasteful but it does not mean that because there are 5 V in a 6 V battery only a sixth of its capacity has been spent and five/sixths remains. When new, the battery capacity is nearer 7 V, but it soon drops to 6 V after a short period of use. It then gradually falls to about 4.5 V and thereafter the fall is rapid and will be accompanied by increasing internal resistance which means that the volts will go down even more when a load is applied. So, most of the useful life of the battery lies above the 5 V point.

It is possible to use up lantern type batteries which have been discarded from the alarm in a torch until they are fully exhausted rather than throw them away. This achieves maximum utilisation and is well worth doing. Alternatively, discarded batteries could be used to run the door bell. One snag with using lantern batteries is that the terminals, which consist of two springs, are rather inconvenient to connect. The best way of dealing with these is to straighten the end of the spring and fit a strip-type flex connector to the wire (see *Figure 4.5*).

Rechargeable batteries

The idea of using rechargeable batteries is attractive in the interests of avoiding the costs of replacing dry ones. The two types commercially available are the lead/acid type as used for car batteries, and the nickel/cadmium variety also known as NiCad units.

Lead/acid batteries are capable of giving heavy discharge for prolonged periods and would be ideal as a standby with a system having heavy loop current. If the mains should fail, they could deliver the loop current for a long period and still have a reserve for the bell should it be needed. Much would depend on the size of the battery, a unit the same size as the dry battery it replaced would have little extra capacity although it would not polarise. A small car battery would give plenty of reserve but would have to be accomodated outside the control unit. This could lead to security difficulties unless leads were passed into some locked cupboard or other compartment. Even if a small lead/acid battery were used, it would be inadvisable to operate it inside the control unit. Acid fumes may be liberated which could corrode components and wiring, and hydrogen gas is given off which could be ignited by a spark from the relay or switching.

These batteries do not like prolonged periods of inactivity or very low discharges, and long life can be obtained only by fairly frequent discharging and charging. Even so, as car owners are well aware, they have a limited life, and have to be replaced after a few years. In the latter part of their life they tend to be unreliable and will not hold a charge for very long after charging.

The nickel cadmium cells are rather less 'messy', being sealed units like ordinary dry batteries. Fully charged, the cell voltage is 1.24 V which means that ten cells would be required to provide 12 V. As voltage stays fairly constant during discharge, there is no need to allow for a drop at the end of the discharge, so eight or nine cells could be sufficient. NiCad batteries are rather fussy over charging conditions, having a low internal resistance, they are easily overcharged and damaged. Special chargers with current regulation are therefore required. The cost of these cells is high, around six or seven times that of the equivalent Leclanché cell.

Giving due consideration to all these factors, it may be concluded that rechargeable batteries offer little saving over dry ones for alarm circuits.

5

Sensors

Sensors are a vital part of any alarm system. These are the guardians that respond to any disturbance caused by an intruder and trigger the main alarm circuit. Having done this they play no further part in the operation as the latching circuit in the control unit takes over to keep the alarm sounding. Hence any attack on the sensor or its wiring after the alarm has sounded is of no avail in silencing the system.

The sensors must be perfectly reliable and operate every time they are actuated, but they must also operate *only* when triggered by an intrusion and not generate false alarms as a result of wind, traffic vibrations and other causes.

Microswitches

Most sensors consist of a switch; either the contacts are normally-open and are closed whan actuated, or they are normally-closed and are opened when operated. Some sensors have two pairs of contacts which change over, one set closes while the other opens; others have three contacts, one being common that switches between the other two. Normally-closed contacts are used in continuous loop arrangements where a current circulates when the system is on guard and cessation of the current triggers the alarm. Normally-open contacts trip the alarm when they are closed, while the changeover three-or four-wire type offer higher security by enabling both types of circuit to be used simultaneously.

The simplest type of sensor is the microswitch (see *Figure 5.1*). As its name implies it is a small switch which can be easily fitted and concealed in door and window frames, shop display units, under stair treads and many other places. It is used in some bell boxes and control units to initiate the alarm if the cover is removed, and can also be used similarly in safes, drawers and cupboards.

Unlike ordinary switches which operate by the up-and-down movement of a lever, the basic microswitch is actuated by a plunger which is sprung so that it is depressed to operate and returns to its at-rest position

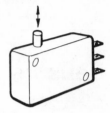

Figure 5.1 Basic microswitch. Arrows show direction of operation

when the pressure is removed. The amount of travel required by the plunger and the pressure needed varies considerably from one switch to another, and selection is determined by the application.

Some makers give full mechanical specifications as to the various parameters of the plunger travel (*Figure 5.2*), and these can be useful

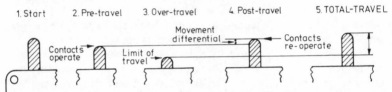

Figure 5.2 Microswitch operation chart showing operating points

when designing a system or selecting a switch for a particular purpose. From the start position, the amount of plunger travel before the switch contacts operate is known as *pre-travel*. The movement from this point onward, is termed *over-travel*, and while a certain amount is necessary to ensure that the contacts are in fact operated, it should not exceed the stipulated *limit-of-travel*.

On the release of the plunger, the travel from the limit to the point where the contacts are re-operated is designated the *post-travel*, and it may be noted that the re-operation point is not exactly the same as the initial operation point, being nearer to the rest position. The difference between the two is termed the *movement-differential*. The distance between the at-rest and limit-of travel positions is logically known as the *total travel*.

The forward stroke is of little interest for alarm applications as the sensor is normally held in the depressed condition, but the release stroke needs consideration. Post-travel must not be too small otherwise vibration and other disturbances may actuate the alarm. Even a door or window with a loose catch may initiate a false alarm as it may not always shut closely. The operating movement of some microswitches is in the order of 0.3 mm which is obviously far too critical for door or window operation. These types are designed for much more sensitive applications. Long travel can be tolerated for sensors on doors and windows as these need to be opened wide to permit entry, and this will reduce the risk of false alarms. For sealed boxes a shorter travel can be selected.

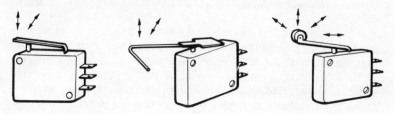

Figure 5.3 Microswitch attachments. Arrows show operating directions. (left) Leaf or lever actuator. (centre) Wire actuator. (right) Roller actuator

The basic switch is often supplemented with an external attachment to alter the mode of operation (*Figure 5.3*). There are three main types, the leaf or lever attachment, wire actuator and roller attachment.

The leaf or lever attachment is hinged at one end and passes over the plunger so that movement of the free end actuates it. The effect is to amplify the amount of movement needed to operate the switch, and the longer the lever, the greater the movement required. Various lengths from 18 mm to 76 mm can be obtained.

The basic microswitch must only be operated by vertical pressure on the plunger, any movement with a sideways or wiping action could deform, jam or break it. Such movement is permissible with a lever, but it must be in one direction only and that is away from the hinge for the downward stroke. Some makers have models with adjustable hinge positions so that leverage and travel can be varied accordingly.

The second attachment is also a lever but instead of a flat blade it consists of a stiff wire with a right-angled bend at the free end. The operation is the same as for the bladed lever but the wire serves more as a feeler. A thin twine trip cord could be attached to the wire or it can be used wherever a sensitive touch is required.

Neither of these devices can be used where a sliding contact is required. For this the roller type of attachment is necessary. Rollers are usually mounted on the end of levers, but they are available fitted into the actual plunger. These have a particular application with casement sliding windows and sliding doors. The advantage is that they can be fitted into the frame a few inches from the end which enables the door or window to be left open by that amount for ventilation or access by a cat or dog. If the door or window is opened any further by a would-be intruder, the microswitch is activated and the alarm is given. It should be added, that leaving a downstairs window open is an invitation for burglars even if it sets off the alarm. If intruders are observant enough to notice the microswitch after the alarm had gone off, they could try again another day, this time armed with a block of wood to slide up the casement when the window is raised, and thus hold the switch in the off position.

A bedroom window which would normally be left open at night in warm weather, could be treated in this way and thus protect the occupants against the unpleasant consequences of finding an intruder in their bedroom. Even so it should be shut and fastened when the owner is absent. Sliding internal doors could also be rigged so that a cat or dog could pass through a small opening but the alarm would be triggered if the gap were widened to admit a human.

Most microswitches have a pressure rating, ranging between ¼-16 oz. Often two figures are given, an operating pressure and maintaining pressure. For door and window sensors the pressure is not too critical, although it should not be too great otherwise it might actually hold off the actuating surface. Where a more delicate touch is required, a unit with a lighter operating pressure will be needed.

Various fixing arrangements are possible as there are different fixing hole placements. Some have holes passing through the sides for sideways fitting, others have holes through the top plate for flush mounting while others have a screwed bush through which the plunger passes for single-hole panel mounting. In spite of their size microswitches have high current ratings, but this is of little importance as most alarm circuits require currents much smaller than the ratings. Operating life is normally high, being rated in the tens of millions of switching cycles. Assuming a door is opened or shut ten times a day a switch with a rated life of ten million operations should last for over 2000 years. Thus for alarm applications, there should be negligible wear with normal usage.

The majority of switches are made with SPDT contacts, that is single-pole, double-throw, or changeover contacts. There are three contacts with these, contact A breaks with contact B and makes with contact C, which is like the twin pair, one normally open and the other closed but with one contact common to both switches. This affords a choice of either open or closed circuit operation, or the high-security double circuit where the control unit will allow a common connection.

Magnetic switches

Microswitches, although quite suitable for certain applications have their limitations, especially as door and window sensors. Whilst good quality units have a long life if subject to normal use, they are vulnerable to damage, either accidental or deliberate. Carelessness in carrying furniture or other bulky objects through a doorway for example could result in a broken or jammed plunger or lever, and high pressure beyond the limit-of-travel can damage the switch.

A would-be intruder having access to the premises during the day could jam a microswitch with chewing gum. As the switch would thus be held in the same position as for a closed door or window, it would not register a fault when the system was tested prior to the switch-on.

Figure 5.4 Reed magnetic switch. Reed contacts are sealed in a glass tube and are actuated by external magnetic field

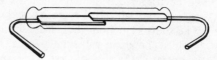

The vulnerability arises because mechanical movement is required to operate the sensor and the actuating portion is unprotected and accessible. Ideally, a sensor should have no external moving parts and be completely protected by its surroundings. These qualities are closely achieved in the magnetic reed switch (see *Figure 5.4*). This consists of a pair of leaf contacts completely sealed in a glass tube. Each contact is supported at opposite ends of the tube with a small overlapping area in the middle where contact is made. When the device is actuated by an external magnetic field, the contacts become temporarily magnetised and attracted to each other and so they close. When the field is removed they are demagnetised and spring apart.

The switch is encapsulated in a plastic case and mounted in the door or window frame. A matching case containing a bar magnet is fitted to the door or window so that when closed the magnet lies adjacent to the switch. Thus the switch contacts are magnetised and so are closed, and can therefore be connected in a closed-loop circuit. When the door or window is opened, the magnet moves away and the switch contacts open.

This arrangement offers numerous advantages over the microswitch. Having no external moving parts it is less vulnerable to damage and it is more difficult to defeat. It does not rely on actual contact with the door and therefore is not affected by vibration, or by minor irregularities such as wood swelling or contracting. There are no restrictions as to the angle of travel of the magnet either toward or away from the switch. The only possible disadvantage, is that two units must be installed instead of one. Positioning and distance between the units is not as critical as with the microswitch and its actuating surface. In fact there can be quite a gap between door and frame without causing problems which is a distinct advantage with older property.

The distance at which the magnet will influence the switch varies according to the type of switch and strength of the magnet. Two distances are quoted by the makers, *operating distance* and *release distance*.

The former is the distance at which the approaching magnet will cause the contacts to close, and the latter the distance at which the receding magnet will allow them to open. The release distance is roughly one-and-a-half times the operating distance, but in some cases it can be over twice as far. For door and window sensors it is the release distance which is the significant parameter.

Typical release distances can be from 10 mm to 35 mm. These represent the distances that the door or window will open before the alarm will be triggered, assuming the units were in close contact with each other to start with. If they were not close, the initial spacing would have to be subtracted from the release distance to find the opening distance at which the alarm will sound. Initial spacing must always be less than the operating distance otherwise the contacts will not close.

The distances quoted by the makers are subject to a certain tolerance between individual units and are measured with a new magnet. As magnetism is lost with age, distances will be reduced as time passes. To ensure reliable operation at all times and with all units of a particular type, minimum distances should be reduced by 25%.

Switch contacts are of precious metal and being sealed in are not affected by atmospheric moisture or pollution. They have therefore an extremely long life, up to 100 million operations or some ten times that of the microswitch. Although such a life is never likely to be achieved when used as door sensors, it does give some indication of the high reliability of the magnetic reed switch, and is a further reason why it is now always used for this purpose in alarm systems.

In addition to the simple two-contact switches there are three-contact changeover switches which enable the device to be used in the normally-open mode instead of in a closed loop, or for higher security, both at the same time. Also there are four-contact switches for use where the control unit does not permit a common wire, and a four-wire system is required. There are different encapsulations to suit different mounting applications which are described in the following paragraphs.

Figure 5.5 Circular magnetic switch and matching magnet

The circular flush-mounting type is inserted into a round hole drilled into the frame with a flat disc on the surface. The circular magnet is lodged in a similar hole drilled in the door (*Figure 5.5*). The result is inconspicuous and the drilling for the units and access for the connecting wires is the only woodwork needed. As the units are around 35 mm long, there must be at least this depth of wood to accomodate them. It may not therefore be possible to use this type for windows or glass doors.

Another factor is that as the mating surface area is small, the switch and the magnet must be accurately aligned to each other.

Another type for flush fitting is the shallow oblong variety (*Figure 5.6*). As these are only a few millimetres deep they can be installed where the wood is not very thick such as in window frames. A cavity must be chiselled out to accomodate them and they are supported by

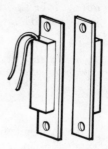

Figure 5.6 Flush-mounted shallow rectangular magnetic switch and matching magnet

screws through the overlapping faceplate. The faceplate normally is above the wood surface, but if a really unobtrusive job is desired, this too can be recessed into the wood and if puttied in and painted over it can be indistinguishable. As the mating area is quite large, accuracy in lining up the switch and magnet is not so important.

There is also an oblong surface fitting type as shown in *Figure 5.7*. These are mounted on the surface of the door frame, opening side, and the magnet unit on the door surface so that they mate edge to edge.

Figure 5.7 Surface mounted magnetic switch and magnet

Being visible and accessible these are less secure than the flush mounting ones. Flush fitting is recommended in all cases where this is possible; where there are metal doors or windows, only the surface mounting units can be fitted.

Although difficult, it is not impossible to defeat a reed switch by using an external magnet. If the intruder knows the position of the switch, and the release distance is sufficient to enable the door to be opened slightly without setting off the alarm, he may be able to insert a small bar magnet over the switch and thus hold it in the 'on' position. The door can then be fully opened and the magnet retained by chewing gum or adhesive tape.

It can be seen that recessing a flush-mounting switch, making good the surrounding woodwork and painting can greatly add to the security as it is then very difficult to find the exact position, especially with the door opened only a few millimetres or less than an inch. If there is a gap between door and frame it may be possible to insert a flat piece of magnetised steel at the switch position if that can be determined, without even the risk of opening the door a fraction, but again it would be impossible to locate the position of a recessed, well camouflaged unit.

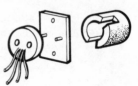

Figure 5.8 High-security double-reed switch. Can only be actuated by both poles of a magnet, hence the bifurcated magnet shape

To further reduce the possibility of defeating a reed switch by an external magnet, there is a high security type which contains two reed contacts which need energising by both poles of a magnet (*Figure 5.8*). The mating magnet is circular, but is divided by a central slot, and the opposite poles are formed by each segment, rather like a horseshoe magnet. These segments are lined up to the two sets of reeds and so actuate them. A bar magnet or piece of magnetised steel will not operate the switch and so it cannot be neutralised by this means. These switches should be installed for high security where determined efforts to beat the system may be tried, but the difficulties in defeating the ordinary switches, especially flush-mounted ones, make the latter perfectly adequate for most domestic installations.

It should be noted that with all magnetic switches the close proximity of ferrous metal objects may affect the operation, particularly the operating distances.

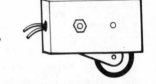

Figure 5.9 Microswitch operated by heavy duty roller for garage doors, etc

Some applications need a particularly robust unit that will stand knocks and adverse conditions. Roller shutters, up-and-over garage doors, bank shutters and similar situations are those calling for specially strong encapsulation. Switches and magnets are available that are sealed in an aluminium case with a low profile outline, and are designed for such purposes.

As an alternative there is a microswitch housed in a steel case, that is actuated by a strong rubber-tyre wheel which partially protrudes from the case. This is illustrated in *Figure 5.9* and is mounted to engage on a rolling or running surface, the switch being operated in less than one revolution.

Pressure mats

These are rectangular flexible pads that come in a wide variety of sizes but usually with an area of between 3-5 ft^2 (0.2-0.4m^2). There are also smaller mats that can be used on stairs. Pressure mats are made up of a large number of contacts spread over the area of the mat so that pressure on any part will close contacts; when the pressure is released, the contacts open. A pvc covering completely seals the unit so that it is protected against dirt and moisture. The lead-out wires are brought through the case thus necessitating a joint to the external wiring. Care should be taken when installing to ensure that the case is not punctured or torn as, although not affecting its immediate operation, it could cause trouble later.

Thickness is typically about ¼ in (5 mm) and the mat should be installed under a carpet or rug where it will not be detected. The thicker the carpet and underfelt, the less noticeable the swelling caused by the mat. On laying, the bulge may seem obvious especially to anyone who knows it is there, but it tends to bed down in time to a hardly perceptible rise in the carpet contour. On stairs, the mat covers the whole of one tread and so is undetectable beneath the stair carpet.

In most cases pressure mats are used as a second line of defence. If by some means an intruder gains entry without setting off the sensors on exterior doors and windows, he will almost certainly step on a pressure mat if strategically placed. Correct placing is all-important in the use of these mats, as they should be located where it is certain that an intruder will step. They can be used for added protection to specific areas of high risk such as in front of safes, silver-collection cabinets, trophies, cups, etc. They can also be used to guard particular areas in commercial premises. In some cases it may be impracticable to guard certain doors or windows with the usual sensors, and pressure mats placed just inside will take over the job.

The amount of pressure needed to actuate a mat is rarely quoted by the makers, but there is a minimum otherwise the weight of the carpet would operate it. This is well below the weight of the lightest person, so there is no danger of failure to trigger the alarm because the intruder is too light. A question may arise as to whether pet dogs or cats may actuate the mat. Different types obviously vary, but in general, a light animal such as a cat or small dog may not actuate the alarm, but a larger dog very likely would do so. A typical mat will actuate at a pressure of between 2.5-3 lb per sq in, so in addition to weight, it also depends on the area over which the weight is distributed. One leg of a dining chair will not normally operate the contacts, but a castor on an easy chair will because, as well as the extra weight, the pressure area is much less.

The average area of a man's shoe sole and heel is about 25 sq in which for a 10-stone weight gives a pressure of 5.6 lb per sq. in. A woman is lighter than a man on average, but the shoe area is usually less so she may exert a larger pressure than a man. A child's weight is less but so also is its shoe area. These figures assume that the foot is laid gently and evenly on the mat; in practice, part of the foot, usually the heel comes down first and there is some momentum behind the action. All this results in a much higher pressure being applied, so there is no chance of a mat being stepped on and failing to respond.

One drawback with pressure mats is that most are normally-open devices and actuation closes the contacts. This means that they cannot be part of a closed loop, and so cannot be tested along with the door sensors each time the alarm is set. The only test is to actually operate each one occasionally by treading on it. With some control units this can be done without sounding the external bell. The control unit must have the open as well as closed circuit sensor facility for mats to be used.

Most domestic systems can be completely served by either the magnetic reed switch or the pressure mat. Hence the majority of domestic alarm kits include four or five reed switches and one or two pressure mats. These are by no means the only types of sensor that are available and some other types are described below.

Conductive strip

For protecting areas of glass, apart from ordinary windows where other sensors would be fitted, strips of metal foil can be used (*Figure 5.10*). These are usually made of aluminium, but lead is also available for use

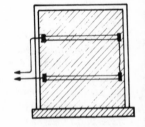

Figure 5.10 Window with two connected metal foil strips. Being visible, the metal foil warns intending intruders and so can prevent breakage

in an area where atmospheric pollutants may corrode the aluminium. Strips are supplied in either self-adhesive or non-adhesive versions, but the self-adhesive is most convenient for normal applications. Various widths are obtainable, the most common being $\frac{1}{8}$ in, $\frac{1}{4}$ in, and $\frac{3}{8}$ in (3, 6 and 8 mm).

The foil strip is run along the inside of the glass and is connected into the closed loop circuit. If the glass is broken, the foil is severed and the loop open-circuited. A single strip across the glass is sufficient for small panes but two or more may be required for large ones. Terminal blocks can be obtained for mounting at the side of the glass to connect the circuit wires to the strip. Also making-off strip is available for bridging two panes of glass across a window frame.

Ideally the strip should be run across the centre of the pane either horizontally or vertically, but this may not be aesthetically pleasing. An alternative which leaves the centre clear, gives adequate protection and can even appear as an embellishment, is to run two strips at roughly a quarter and three quarter positions up the glass. A further advantage is that the circuit wires can be connected at the same side of the window, the free ends being linked on the opposite side by wire along the frame.

An important feature of metal foil on glass is that it can be seen from the outside. An intending intruder can therefore see that the glass is protected by an alarm and knows that there is no point in breaking it to try to gain entry. This is better than letting the intruder break in before realising the window is protected by an alarm. Glass is expensive, as well as the cost of replacement, so prevention is better than cure.

There are obvious problems associated with fitting metal foil to windows that open. The connecting block would have to be fitted to the window on the hinge side and flexible leads bridged over to another block on the frame to connect to the circuit wiring. It is probably best therefore to use a magnetic sensor for opening windows.

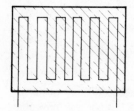

Figure 5.11 Wired glass consisting of two bonded sheets with silvered wire at 2-in (50 mm) spacing

While in most cases metal foil offers good protection, it is not unassailable. A determined intruder could use a glass cutter to cut a hole in the pane avoiding the metal strips. He may then reach a fastening on that or an adjacent window through the hole. With a showcase containing valuables, the thief may be able to abstract the contents through the hole. One remedy would be to run many strips close together, but this would greatly restruct visibility. An alternative is to use wired glass as shown in *Figure 5.11*. This is special glass consisting of two sheets sealed together with a series of silver wires across almost the complete width. The wire is very fine and so in not obtrusive, but being spaced about 2 in (50 mm) apart gives maximum protection. As with the foil, the wire is connected into a closed loop. This is obviously more expensive than foil which can be fitted to existing glass but it affords higher security where this is needed.

The same idea can be used to protect ceilings. These are often overlooked as a means of entry, but with single-story premises it is comparatively easy to gain access to the roof, remove a few tiles and enter by breaking through the ceiling. A fine wire can be run to and fro across the ceoiling, then papered over to give complete and inexpensive protection. The wire should be varnished to protect it against corrosion, the type used for transformer winding being particularly suitable.

Vibration contacts

The vibration contact is a pendulum with contacts mounted in close proximity, sealed into a rectangular plastic case. Usually it is fitted to large areas of glass such as shopwindows where it would be unacceptable to use an adequate number of metal foil runs for protection.

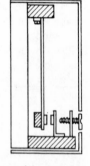

Figure 5.12 Basic principle of vibration detector. Pendulum contact in close proximity to fixed contact. The latter is movable to give adjustment of sensitivity by screw

If the glass is broken, the vibration moves the unit and hence the contacts. The pendulum remains stationary, so the relative movement between contacts and pendulum actuates the switch (see *Figure 5.12*). Units are obtainable in either single-or double-pole versions. A means of adjusting the spacing between pendulum and contacts is provided so that the device can be set to respond to either small or large vibrations.

In a shop window, the contact cannot be set too finely as it then could be triggered by passing traffic or even window shoppers. This is the principal disadvantage of the vibration contact. An advantage is that it will respond (if not set too coarsely) to an attempted break-in. Shop windows of toughened glass will stand up to a certain amount of attack. A blow which proved unsuccessful in breaking the glass could set off the alarm and deter any further attempt.

Vibration contacts can be used for purposes other than protecting glass. Any structure not easily protected by conventional sensors but which could be subject to forcing or blows to effect entry, could be fitted with vibration contacts. In a normally quiet or vibration-free environment, the sensitivity can be finely set to give an alarm at the first efforts at interference. In any given application the success depends largely on the correct adjustment.

Acoustic detectors

Also called sonic detectors, these are not to be confused with the ultrasonic devices described in the next chapter. The term embraces a range of sensors that operate by sound generated by the forced entry (*Figure 5.13*). Commonly this is of breaking glass, and while other sensors can be used to detect this, the acoustic detector does have certain advantages.

Figure 5.13 (a) Small acoustic detector for fixing to glass. Responds only to sounds of breaking glass. (b) Non-contact acoustic detector detects sounds of breaking glass over 15 ft

(a)   *(b)*

The main advantage is that the unit is made to respond *only* to those sound frequencies resulting from breaking glass; in one model the frequencies are from 6-8 kHz, which is very high (top note of the piano is just over 4 kHz). The restriction of the response to this limited range means that the device will not operate for other sounds and so is not so susceptible to false alarms as is the vibration contact.

The detector consists of a microphone, built-in transistor amplifier and filter circuits to pass only the desired frequency range. Size has been reduced to a minimum, in some cases the device is of only a little larger diameter than a 50p coin. These types are fixed to the window by an adhesive. Other detectors are not fixed directly to the glass but are mounted in a convenient position nearby. The microphone picks up any sound of glass breaking over a range of about 15 ft (4.5 m) and separate panes can be protected by the one sensor. One device has an indicator lamp which lights when it is activated. This assists in rapidly locating the cause of an alarm where there are a variety of sensors on large premises.

In the case of the detectors that are stuck on to the glass, the microphone is a contact type. This does not pick up sound waves through the air but sound vibrations are conducted directly to the crystal generating-unit inside the detector. This is similar to the crystal gramophone pickup where vibrations from the record groove are transmitted to the crystal via the stylus.

An extension of this principle is found in the wall sound detector unit. Sounds picked up by the microphone are filtered to produce an alarm signal only from percussive sources such as hammering, drilling and cutting. These all produce high frequencies which are passed by the filters, whereas low frequencies such as traffic noise are blocked. Some of these detector systems have facilities for a number of microphones to be connected to them, and thus form almost a complete alarm system in themselves covering quite large areas that are physically separated. The master unit receives the output from the microphones, filters and amplifies it, and produces a signal which is fed into the main alarm circuit to trigger it.

Acoustic detectors are more than just switches like the other sensors we have discussed, because they amplify and process the signal by transistor circuitry, and hence need a power supply. This is supplied by the master unit, or in the case of the simple single detector, from the alarm system control unit. When considering the use of acoustic detectors it must be first ascertained whether the control unit will work with them.

There is little need for this type of sensor in domestic installations, but for commercial premises containing valuable stock where thieves may go to considerable trouble to gain entry, they can protect ceilings and walls which could provide access.

Inertia detectors

The inertia detector senses movement or vibration, and so is not unlike the vibration contact, but it is better at detecting low frequency movements. It can be used for protecting glass and walls and also by sensing movement on doors, gates, fences, etc.

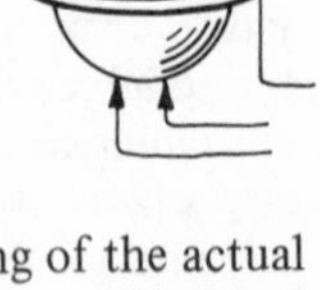

Figure 5.14 Inertia detector. A ball rests on two contacts forming closed circuit. An extra ring contact surrounds ball. It is used for detecting motion and vibration

Inertia detectors are usually part of a system consisting of the actual sensors and the analyser module. One make of sensor uses a gold-plated ball seated on a pair of contacts thereby forming a normally-closed switch, any movement breaks the contact. A high-security version of this sensor has, in addition, a ring around the ball which serves as a normally-open contact; a disturbance produces a contact between ball and ring (*Figure 5.14*). Thus the sensor has both normally-closed and normally-open contacts and so can form part of a three-or four-wire system. Where background vibration may be high, sensors that are magnetically damped should be used to avoid false alarms.

If the current in the circuit where these sensors are used is high, deformation of the contact points could take place. This is because the contact area of a ball is very small so the heating effect caused by a spark is concentrated in that area. Any resulting pitting or protrubérance would impair the future operation of the device, while for very high currents, the ball may even become welded to the contact.

In the case of the model described above, maximum current is specified as 0.2 mA at an applied voltage not exceeding 2 V. This is in contrast with the vibration-contact which will pass up to half-an-amp at 250 V. Unlike the vibration contacts, inertia sensors cannot be used directly with most control units unless they have a very low loop current.

Normally, inertia detectors are operated with their own analyser modules. These supply the low loop current required and include a sensitivity control which sets the level of vibration to which the system will respond. The frequency response of the sensors is much lower than the glass acoustic detectors described in the last section, being in the region of 10 Hz-1.5 kHz. (1 kHz = 1000 Hz), and this enables them to respond to physical motion and jarring.

For outdoor fence protection a string of sensors is required spaced at about 10 ft (3 m) intervals. Any attempt to damage or climb the fence will be detected, but there is a problem of possible false alarms by animals, children playing, or sundry objects falling against or being blown onto the fence. To overcome this some analysers have counting circuits which count the number of impulses received from the sensors in a specified time. The alarm is only triggered if they exceed a set number, indicating that an intruder was attempting to gain access. Random impulses from casual causes will in most cases fall short of the critical number. Typical values for daytime operation are 8 impulses in 30 sec. For night protection, casual disturbances will be far fewer and the degree of protection needed greater, so the circuit can be set to respond with an alarm for a much smaller number of impulses. This may be as low as 4 in 15 min.

The analysers are themselves controlled by a control unit and they may be, and probably are in most cases, mounted near the sensors and remote from the control unit. Some analysers automatically reset after an alarm, the reset time being adjustable, while others need to be reset from the control unit. Units with counting circuits have night/day changeover relays which change the number of impulses counted to produce an alarm.

It can be seen that to use inertia sensors effectively, elaborate control circuitry must be employed. In many cases vibration sensors will do the job just as well. However for protecting perimeter walls or fences, especially wire mesh types, the inertia detector is undoubtedly the best sensor.

Safe limpets

These are sensors designed to protect safes from attack, but can be used on filing cabinets and equipment consoles. Several types are available, but most are fitted magnetically to the unit being protected (see *Figure 5.15*).

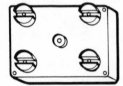

Figure 5.15 Safe limpet containing vibration and magnetic switch

The simplest type contains a vibration detector which operates if an attempt is made to force the safe open. It also includes a contact which is held in place magnetically as long as the unit is fixed to the safe. If it is removed, the contacts operate and the alarm is triggered. Another type utilises an inertia sensor which responds to low frequencies as well as the higher ones.

A third type includes a thermal switch as well as vibration contacts. This detects an abnormal rise in temperature as would be produced by a thermal lance or other metal cutting equipment.

Photo-electronic detectors

These are a rather specialised sensors for use in a normally darkened area such as a vault or a strongroom. Though they can be used in any window-less situation that needed protection. In such a situation, an intruder will obviously use a torch, and the reflected light will actuate the sensor.

Sensitivity is adjustable down to less than 1 lux. Light from a match or thermal lance is sufficient to actuate it. The sensor has single-pole changeover contacts which means that it can be used either as a normally-open or normally-closed device, or both. A 12 V d.c. supply is needed to power the electronic circuit, and this must be provided by the control unit.

A number of sensors can be used if required to cover a large area or individual positions. While these would not take the place of sensors to detect entry, they could form a valuable 'back-up' system where maximum security is essential.

Diode sensor-muting

Returning now to the loop with conventional reed or microswitch contacts, a weak point is the vulnerability of the loop wiring during the day in premises to which strangers could have easy access. To confuse intending tamperers three-or four-wire systems are used as described in an earlier chapter, and the sensors include both open and closed contacts.

If now an attempt at defeating the loop was made sometime during the day, and was unsuccessful, i.e. the wrong wires were bridged or cut, a fault would be indicated as soon as the alarm was tested or switched on at the end of the day. Although the tampering is thus brought to light, the key-holder must now remain on the premises while technical help is obtained to locate the damage and put it right. This may take some while and the key-holder, probably being the only person on the premises, may thus be liable to attack by the intruder who tampered with the wiring, returning in anticipation of such a situation.

If technical help cannot be obtained at this time, it may mean the premises being left without an alarm for the night, again playing into the hands of the intruder. Even if the damage is put right without incident, an inconvenient delay will have been suffered by the key-holder.

One way in which this situation can be prevented is by monitoring the loop throughout the day so that any damage, deliberate or accidental will give an alarm even though the contacts are being operated by people opening and closing doors during the normal course of business.

This is done by shunting each contact with a diode (see *Figure 5.16*). As described in a previous chapter this passes current in one direction

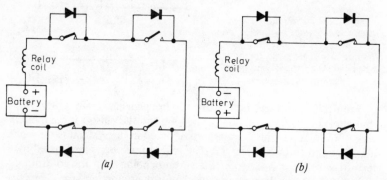

Figure 5.16 (a) Diode muting of loop sensors for day-time monitoring. Polarity of battery is such that diodes conduct and so loop is continuous whether sensor contacts are opened or closed. Cutting the wiring breaks the loop and sounds the day alarm immediately. (b) Battery polarity is reversed for night alarm service. Diodes no longer conduct and loop functions normally

but not the other. So if the battery polarity is reversed across a circuit containing a diode, current will cease if it had been flowing previously.

For daytime loop monitoring, the battery in the control circuit is connected so that the diodes effectively short-circuit the contacts. Thus the loop is continuous whether the contacts are open or shut. A sensing current is passed around the loop in the normal way and it is not interrupted by doors or windows being opened and shut. Only if the wiring is damaged will the current cease and the alarm be sounded.

At night, the battery polarity is reversed by suitable switching in the control unit, whereupon the diodes no longer conduct and the loop and its contacts behave normally. If desired one or more contacts can be left unbridged to give 24 hour protection to a high security area. Access to this could then only be obtained by a key-operated shunt-switch.

This arrangement obviously offers a high degree of security where there is a possibility of daytime tampering with the wiring. The alarm bell operative during the day need not be the main one, but could be a small bell or buzzer located where those responsible for security will hear it; switching from one to the other can be accomplished by the day and night switch on the control unit.

There is the question of whether the diodes themselves constitute a reliability hazard should any one fail. Some diodes are more reliable than others, but all are subject to the possibility of failure. In nearly every case though, a defective diode will go open-circuit rather than short-circuit. Thus it will fail safe and the effect will be to sound the daytime alarm when the affected door is opened, as the sensor is unmuted.

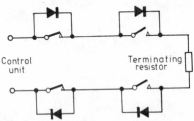

Figure 5.17 Diode muted loop using terminating resistor. This foils attempts at bridging across loop as alrm is triggered for both open and short-circuit conditions (Monive System)

Control unit

Terminating resistor

Even this circuit can be defeated by bridging across any of the wires thus shorting out that section of the loop and the sensors it contains. A way of overcoming this possibility is adopted in the system used by one maker as shown in *Figure 5.17*. The end of the loop is terminated by a resistor which is connected at the furthest point from the control unit and will appear in the circuit about half-way around the loop. Thus the resistance of the loop will be within certain limits. If the resistance becomes much higher, i.e. an open-circuit, loop current drops below normal or ceases and the alarm is triggered. Also, if the resistance becomes lower due to an attempt at bridging, loop current increases and this too triggers the alarm. Any change in resistance greater than $2\,k\Omega$ either higher or lower, produces an alarm condition. Thus a very high degree of security is obtained as it is virtually impossible to tamper with the wiring without sounding the alarm.

Carrying further the principle of using a terminating resistor an alternative system devised by the same maker is a loop using normally-open contacts (*Figure 5.18*). The loop is formed by the wiring which is looped

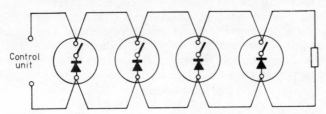

Figure 5.18 Resistor-terminated loop using parallel normally-open sensors. Muting diodes are in series with each contact but not in series with each other. This enables unlimited number of diode-muted sensors to be used in the loop
(Monive System)

from one pair of sensor contacts to the next and is completed by the terminating resistor. The sensor contacts are therefore across the loop instead of being in series and when a contact closes, the loop resistance is shorted out. The daytime muting diodes are connected *in series* with each contact and so renders it open-circuit when the battery polarity is reversed.

The advantage of this arrangement is that any number of diode muted sensors can be connected to the circuit. Diodes possess a certain resistance even in the forward connection, so with the series loop the resistance of each diode is added to the total in the circuit. This limits the number that can be used to either ten germanium diodes or four silicon diodes.

With the shunt-connected sensors, the diodes are not in series with each other, only with its own sensor contacts, and so they do not add to the total resistance of the circuit. As with the series circuit, one or more contacts can be left without a diode to give round-the-clock protection to certain areas.

There are, however, some drawbacks to this circuit; being normally-open contacts, the sensors cannot easily be tested other than by individual operation, whereas the series loop can be tested by passing a test current through the sensors themselves. While it is the wiring that is most vulnerable, sensors, especially microswitches could become jammed or otherwise damaged. The other snag is that being in series with the sensor, an open-circuit diode would render it inoperative, and as pointed out before, an open-circuit is the most likely fault for a diode to develop. As the sensors are not readily tested, this could pass undetected for some period. The series circuit therefore offers the higher security, but the number of sensors that can be used is limited.

Conclusion

From the descriptions in this chapter it can be seen that there is a considerable choice of sensors to suit the many and varied possibilities of entry and type of area to be protected. Some can be used for several applications while others are quite specific in their purpose.

These are not the only methods of detecting intrusion and some more elaborate systems are discussed in the next chapter.

6

Active Detection Systems

The sensors described in the last chapter could all be classified as *passive* devices, they operate as a result of a signal generated by the intruder; noise, vibration, pressure, light, or movement of a door or other object. The devices examined in this chapter generate their own signal which is radiated into the protected area and received back again, the alarm responding to any differences produced by the presence of an intruder. They could therefore be termed *active* detectors.

The main types of system are: ultrasonic, microwave and infra-red, and there are some less well-known types as well. Most of these operate by *Doppler effect*, so for readers unfamiliar with this, a brief explanation is given below.

The Doppler effect

If we were to stand on the beach at the seaside while waves were coming in at regular intervals, we could count the number of waves per minute reaching us, and this we could term their *frequency*. If instead of remaining stationary, we started to swim out to sea, we would be meeting the waves and as we would encounter more per minute than when we were standing still, the frequency would increase. On the other hand if we were to swim toward the shore, we are going with the waves and fewer would actually pass us, we might even surf in on the crest of a single wave. Thus the frequency has decreased.

The same is true of any type of wave generator, if we move towards it, the frequency to us increases, but when we move away the frequency drops. It is not important whether the observer or the generator moves; if there is relative movement between them there will be a frequent shift. A familiar example of this effect is the police or ambulance siren which sounds lower pitched when moving away from the listener than when it is approaching; the pitch of the sound being governed by the frequency of the sound waves.

Ultransonic detectors

The term 'ultrasonic' denotes sound frequencies that are above the range of human hearing, the upper limit of which is about 16 kHz. The frequencies used in these detectors varies, ranging between 23 and 40 kHz. The principle is that an electronic oscillator generates an ultrasonic frequency which is fed to one or more loudspeakers. Speakers for producing very high frequencies need to be small because the moving parts must move very rapidly and so their mass kept to a minimum. This is an advantage for alarm systems as they then can be made unobtrusive in appearance.

The high frequency sound is produced in the protected area, and it is received back by a microphone usually housed in the same unit as the loudspeaker. The received sound consists both of direct pickup from the loudspeaker and also that reflected from various surfaces in the area.

If there is any movement within the range of the unit, the reflected sound from the moving object will undergo a frequency shift due to Doppler effect. So the microphone will pick up two different frequencies, the original from the loudspeaker and reflected from stationary objects, and the shifted frequency reflected from the moving object. If two nearby frequencies are mixed, a third frequency will be produced which is the difference between them; this is known as a *beat note*. Thus if from the original 23 kHz, a Doppler frequency of 22.7 kHz is reflected, a beat frequency of 0.3 kHz (300 Hz) will appear. A fourth frequency which is the sum of the two frequencies is also generated, but this is too high to be of any practical value for this application.

The frequency of the beat note depends on the speed of the moving reflecting surface relative to the detector unit, but in all cases it will be very much lower than the ultrasonic frequencies that produced it, as in the above example.

The principle is shown in *Figure 6.1*. The microphone output is first passed through a high-pass filter which eliminates any ordinary sound from outside that might be picked up by the microphone, and only passes the ultrasonic ones. Another circuit now analyses the signal for any low-frequency content, if any is present it must be due to a beat note from a Doppler shift. This is separated by a low-pass filter, the output from which is amplified and finally made to operate a relay. The relay contacts can then be wired to any ordinary alarm system. Usually the relay is continually energised and the alarm signal de-energises it. Thus, if the power supply to the unit fails, the relay is de-energised and the alarm is sounded.

The main difference in application between an ultrasonic detector and the sensors described in the last chapter is that the ultrasonic type protects space, while ordinary sensors protect points of entry. With ultrasonic detection anything that moves in the protected area generates an alarm. It can be used therefore as a back-up system either separately, wired to the main system, or to protect space that would be difficult or impractical to protect by entry detectors. It is virtually impossible to defeat the system, as, if it is positioned well away from possible entry

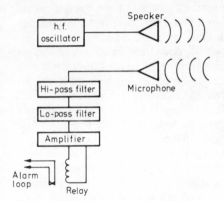

Figure 6.1 Block diagram of ultrasonic detector. High frequencies are produced by the loudspeaker into the protected area. They are reflected back into the microphone the output of which is passed through a high pass filter to eliminate audible sound, then through a low pass filter to extract any beat frequency due to a Doppler shift. If present this indicates a moving object in the area. The beat frequency is amplified and made to operate a relay in the alarm loop circuit

points, movement is essential to approach the unit. Disabling the unit in advance is about the only way to neutralise it, but most models include anti-tamper microswitches to detect daytime interference. Additionally, the fittings are designed to appear unobtrusive and are even disguised to look like something different. Some may look like hi-fi loudspeakers, or industrial intercom speakers, while one domestic unit is even disguised as a book!

Range is nominally between 15-20 ft (4.5-6 m) but this is affected by the nature of the surfaces in the area. If these are hard, i.e. wood, brick, plaster or stone, the range will be extended, but if they are soft and absorbent, such as thick carpets, curtains, and upholstery, the range is reduced. The range is sufficient for most domestic rooms, even large ones, but may be insufficient for many industrial applications, though it can be extended by the use of extra microphones and loud-speakers. Interaction between adjacent speakers or microphones is no problem providing they are phased, i.e. all connected the same way round.

Power requirements vary between models. Some run from batteries, others are mains only, while yet others are mains with battery standby. Current taken from a 12 V battery ranges from 50-100 mA. This is much higher than a low-consumption loop, although not much different from some of the heavy current ones. It is a heavy drain on dry batteries and heavy duty rechargeable batteries would be required for continuous operation. When operating from the mains, consumption is around 1½ W which is very low. The best arrangement is therefore mains operation with battery standby.

The drawback with ultrasonic detectors is that they are prone to false alarms. A Doppler frequency shift can be produced by the air, through which the sound travels, moving as well as a moving reflecting surface. Thus ultrasonic detectors are eliminated from outdoor use as the slightest breeze would give an alarm. Even indoors, there are many sources of air movement which could trigger the alarm. Among these are draughts from doors and windows, downward movement of cold air from windows, convection currents from radiators, and turbulence from air-conditioning and ventilators. Movement of curtains must also be avoided and animals excluded from the area.

Another possible cause of false alarms is that of very high-pitched sounds originating nearby. These may have harmonics extending into the ultrasonic range and so could produce beat notes in the detector. Possible sources are brakes of vehicles on adjacent roads, line-timebase whistle from a nearby television receiver, leaking compressed air lines, water pipes and gas fires. When assessing the conditions at the proposed site, great care must be taken to check whether ultrasonic detection is suitable and not likely to be plagued with false alarms.

After switching on, a delay of anything from 10-30 sec is usually provided for the unit to become active to enable the user to vacate the room. A delay for entry is not necessarily required as the main alarm circuit would be switched off first, but some models provide the facility.

Microwave detectors

Most microwave detectors work in a similar manner to ultrasonic systems except that radio waves are used instead of sound waves. The heart of the generator is a crystal of gallium arsenide known as a Gunn diode. This oscillates at an incredible rate, in most models at around 10.7 GHz, (1 GHz = 10^9 Hz = 1 000 000 kHz). In some units the frequency is 1.5 GHz.

These oscillations are projected in the form of radio waves from a radiator as a beam. Radiated power varies but is usually around 10 mW. The beam is directed into the protected area and reflected signals are detected by a receiver and mixed with the overspill from the transmitter. Any difference in frequency is due to Doppler effect from a moving object and the resulting beat is amplified and used to trigger the alarm.

A feature of microwaves is that they will penetrate wood, glass plaster and even to a limited extent, brick. This can have both advantages and drawbacks. In an area where there are large objects which could give an intruder cover, such as packing cases in a warehouse, the microwaves will pass through them and thus reveal any moving object or person that may be concealed from ultrasonic systems or visual surveillance. This is useful in such a situation where objects may be continually moved around and where it may not be possible to always arrange a clear view from a check point for security staff. It should be noted though that metal objects will reflect microwaves, so machinery would act as a shield.

The disadvantage with this is that the beam will penetrate floor walls and particularly the ceiling and therefore could trigger a false alarm due to moving objects outside the protected area. To overcome this, transmitters can be fitted with deflector plates which give a predetermined beam shape in both horizontal and vertical axes. The vertical axis is usually flat topped like a car headlamp beam so that it does not penetrate the ceiling above. Horizontal distribution can be wide, narrow or even in a split coverage as required.

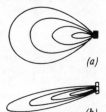

Figure 6.2 Polar diagram of microwave transmitter. Internal lobes indicate coverage when output is reduced. (a) Horizontal plane; (b) Vertical plane

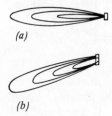

(a)

(b)

Figure 6.3 Narrow beam microwave for long narrow areas. This minimises wall penetration and false alarms. (a) Horizontal plane; (b) Vertical plane

Figure 6.4 Split beam microwave for covering two connected areas with one unit

The range of a microwave system is much greater than that of the ultrasonic detector, being normally from 15-150 ft (4.5 to 45.5 m). To avoid false alarms the beam should be no longer than the enclosure it is to protect. Most systems have facilities to vary the strength, hence range of the radiation. When set to the shorter lengths, the width and height are also reduced in proportion. This is shown by the smaller internal lobes appearing in the polar diagrams (*Figures 6.2 to 6.4*).

Some models are designed to be mounted in the ceiling facing downward (*Figure 6.5*). These have an omnidirectional radiation pattern from the downward face and at a ceiling height of about 10 ft (3 m), give an area of coverage of some 60 ft (18 m) in diameter. The range of these need only be from the centre of the ceiling where the unit should be fitted to the furthest corner of the room and so is around 30 ft (9 m) maximum.

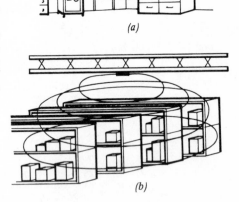

Figure 6.5 Ceiling-mounted microwave unit gives good coverage over limited floor area. There is virtually no penetration outside the area except through the floor. Ideal for ground floor areas. (a) Typical small office area protection. (b) Excellent coverage in factory storage area. Steel racking gives intruder shelter from horizontal beams, but none from overhead radiation

(a)

(b)

As the beams come from overhead, large metal objects such as machinery or filing cabinets afford no cover for an intruder. Coming from this angle the microwaves are not required to penetrate 'soft' objects of wood or similar material. They can therefore be of a lower frequency which gives less penetration, as well as being set to just the range required instead of to a longer range to compensate for the attenuation produced by such penetration. One model does in fact use the lower 1.48 GHz frequency. All this serves to reduce the possibility of false alarms due to objects moving outside the protected area, and so for smaller floor areas with approximately square configurations, the ceiling mounted unit has a lot to commend it.

Microwaves can pass through plastic materials, so the transmitter and receiver unit can be contained within a plain plastic case, or a metal case with a plastic front without giving any hint of its nature. One ceiling model is made for flush-mounting so that all that appears from beneath is a rectangular panel. Some units are fitted to a bracket by means of a ball-and-socket joint so that they can be angled in any direction.

Apart from overranging beyond the required area, there are few possibilities of false alarms. Air disturbance has no effect as it has with ultrasonic devices. Some gas-filled lamps, such as fluorescent and neon lights, may generate radio frequencies which could be accepted by the receiver, but these can be filtered out electronically. Most models incorporate such filters.

Another type of microwave system does not use Doppler effect but transmits a narrow beam to a receiver situated at a remote point which can be anything up to 500 ft (152 m) away (see *Figure 6.3*). An alarm is given if anything breaks the beam. The beam diverges as it travels from the transmitter so its width may be anything from 3-20 ft (1-6 m) at maximum range. It has a built-in 'fail safe' factor as if the transmitter does not function for any reason, the receiver will trigger the alarm.

This system is intended for outdoor use where Doppler effect units are unsuitable because the boundary, consisting of a wooden or wire-mesh fence, is transparent to microwaves. Even where the boundary is a brick wall there would be a considerable escape of microwave radiation over the top. Thus there could be a strong possibility of false alarms due to moving objects outside, unless the range was restricted to fall within the perimeter, in which case the protection is removed just where it is needed — around the points of entry.

The beam-breaking system can be installed so that it transmits just inside and parallel to the boundary fence (*Figure 6.6*). For a typical rectangular enclosure, four transmitter and receiver units would be

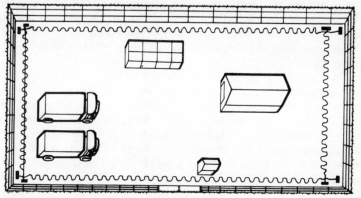

Figure 6.6 Perimeter fence with protection by four sets of beam-breaking microwave units

required, one for each side. This would guard up to 2000 ft (61 km) of boundary fencing, for which the inertia detector system would require some two hundred sensors. The choice between these two systems is obviously governed to a great extent by the size of the enclosure to be protected and also its shape. An irregular perimeter configuration does not lead itself easily to microwave beam breaking protection.

Advantages and disadvantages

Microwaves are attenuated by rain and fog, and outdoor units are usually equipped with automatic gain controls to compensate for this. Another hazard with outdoor installations is that of small objects such as birds, and windborne paper which could break the beam and cause a false alarm. The solution adopted by some makers is to set a minimum size to the beam-breaking object that will cause an alarm. Thus anything of an area below the set minimum will not trigger the alarm.

Like the ultrasonic detector it is virtually impossible to defeat a microwave system that is working, as any approach to the units will be detected. However, a Doppler system could be neutralised by tampering with the unit during the period when it is switched off. If mounted on an adjustable bracket, the unit could be swivelled around to face in another direction or a metal plate could even be fitted over the transmitting face. When switched on, the internal receiver would still get reflections from the plate or wall but none from the protected area and so no movements there would be detected.

The changed position, or deflector plate may go unnoticed in a busy establishment, but where such tampering is possible a microwave monitor can be installed at a point remote from the unit. Being a sensitive receiver, this detects microwaves and generates an alarm signal if none are received. Thus inadvertent shielding of the transmitter unit by a large metal object, which could easily happen in a warehouse, is revealed as well as deliberate interference.

The Gunn diode operates on a low voltage and the rest of the transmitting and receiving circuit is designed to do likewise. Hence microwave systems are usually run at 12 V. Current required is higher than an ultrasonic detector being from 150-250 mA. Mains operation is essential as this current would soon exhaust a battery other than a heavy duty rechargeable type. A battery would, of course, be needed as a standby. In locations where mains power is not available, a car battery would sustain the system for about 80 hours. It could therefore be run with a freshly charged battery every half-week, the old one being recharged for the following period. This would allow a generous margin for 16 hour-a-day operation with a 20 Ah battery.

Infra-red sensors

Infra-red radiation is an electromagnetic emission that lies just below the visible light part of the spectrum, but much higher than normal radio frequencies. Actual frequency range is wider than that of visible light being from approximately 10^{12} to 10^{14} Hz, or 1000 to 100 000 GHz. Fortunately, radiation in this region is easily generated, either by an infra-red lamp which is a blackened filament lamp running at low temperature or, more efficiently by a crystal of gallium arsenide. In the latter case the radiation is sometimes known as 'gallium arsenide rays'.

The system used is that of the beam-breaking type. A narrow ray is transmitted across the entrance to be protected by a projector to a receiver on the other side. If the beam is broken, the receiver triggers the alarm, in similar manner to the outdoor microwave system.

Infra-red radiation is generated by most sources that produce heat as the two are closely related in the spectrum. Thus lamp bulbs, electric and other heaters and even a pocket torch generate infra-red rays to a greater or lesser extent. Any of these could interfere with the system, and an intruder could even defeat it by shining a portable infra-red source toward the receiver as he moved across and broke the original beam. This type of interference is prevented by modulating the radiation from the projector. This means that the ray is not steady but is generated in a series of rapid pulses at a predetermined rate. This rate varies according to the type of equipment but typically is around 200 times per second. The receiver has electronic filters which accept only the modulating frequency, and the triggering relay is held off by the presence of incoming signals of this frequency. If the signals cease, the relay is released and the alarm given, even if a steady infra-red radiation is received in its place.

Figure 6.7 Selection of infra-red units. Projectors, receivers and mirrors are housed in identical cases. Dummy cases are also available to further confuse intruders

Transmitter and receiver units are housed in identical cases, hence as the ray is invisible, it is not possible to identify the units. This further complicates any attempt to defeat the system and can be compounded by the use of additional dummy housings (*Figure 6.7*).

The only way the ray can be evaded is by physically avoiding it, for example by crawling underneath it. To do this the intruder must be aware of its presence and its path, but even so evasion becomes impossible if the beam is 'laced' across the entry point zig-zag fashion. This can be done by means of mirrors on either side; unlike the microwave beam, which is too diffuse, the infra-red ray can be reflected at several points by small reflectors just like a ray of light, so one projector and receiver can protect an irregularly shaped path or be laced across a doorway or gap between buildings as shown in *Figure 6.8.*

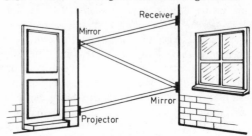

Figure 6.8 Lacing an infra-red beam across an area to make avoidance difficult. Lower units should be closely spaced to prevent intruders stepping through or crawling under the beams. False alarms are possible from wildlife, etc., to avoid this use two parallel beams

The range of infra-red systems varies from a maximum 40 ft (12 m) for small units up to 1000 ft (300 m) for the largest. When reflected from a mirror, the ray is attenuated and so each reflection shortens the range. For 1 reflection the range is reduced to 75%, for 2 reflections it drops to 60% and for 3, it falls to 43%. (*Table 6.1*). It is not recommended that more than three mirrors be used.

The rays will also penetrate clear glass and so the protection can be extended through glass partitions and windows. Here again there is a reduction in range for each glass pane, although the attenuation is less than for mirror reflection. For 20 oz window glass, the range is reduced to 83% for a single sheet, to 70% for 2 sheets, to 60% for 3 sheets and 50% for 4 sheets.

Table 6.1 Transmission losses of infra-red rays, mirror or glass

| Number | Range Reductions | |
	Reflections, %	Penetrations, % (20 oz glass)
1	75	83
2	60	70
3	43	60
4	–	50

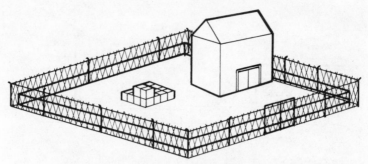

Figure 6.9 Infra-red perimeter system. Mirrors enable one continuous beam, but two beams are used in parallel to avoid false alarms. Should not be used in cold exposed areas where mirrors may be frozen over

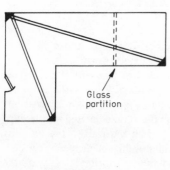

Glass partition

Figure 6.10 Infra-red beam with mirror used to protect irregular areas. Will pass though glass

Figure 6.11 Stairway protection with infra-red beam. Diagonal angling prevents avoidance by keeping to one side

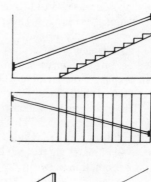

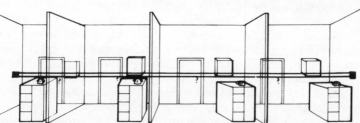

Figure 6.12 A divided office with glass partitions can be protected with a single beam. Opening any of the doors will break the beam. Check that range is sufficient from Table 6.1

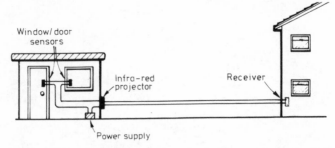

Figure 6.13 Separate alarm system in outbuilding can be tied in to the main alarm by means of infra-red beam. Sensor loop is in series with power supply to projector, so if sensors are actuated projector stops. Receiver on main building then sounds the alarm. Latching circuit is not necessary as this is included in main alarm, so alarm continues even if beam cessation is only momentary. Protection over intervening area is also achieved

This method of protection is therefore versatile. It can be used around perimeters, laced across entrances, beamed down stairways, and across rooms and offices. It can also be used to transmit alarm signals from an auxiliary protected area to the main one. In the latter case, the auxiliary area, say an outbuilding, may have its own alarm sensors but instead of these actuating a separate alarm they could be used to interrupt the power supply to an infra-red projector on the wall of the building which is beamed to a receiver on the main building. This receiver is connected into the main alarm circuit, so that operation of any of the sensors in the outbuilding will switch off the projector, and the receiver deprived of the incoming ray will actuate the main alarm.

This arrangement will also protect the intervening space between the two buildings as anyone crossing the ground will break the beam. Several outbuildings can be included in the system providing each has its projector and matching receiver on the main premises. Besides the bonus of space protection between the buildings, this eliminates the need for connecting wires which could be particularly vulnerable over open ground.

When used outdoors, there is the possibility of the beam being interrupted by birds or windborne objects. The answer to this is to use two projectors and receivers to produce parallel beams spaced 1½-2 ft (450-600 mm) apart. The receiver alarm contacts are then connected in parallel so that if either beam is broken the loop is maintained through the other contacts. Thus small objects will not raise a false alarm. It is only when both beams are broken that both sets of contacts are open and the alarm triggered.

Power requirements are a nominal 12 V, and the current taken is from 50-100 mA depending on type of unit.

Summary of the systems

Looking at the three systems described above, their respective features can now be analysed and comparisons made. Doppler effect devices use ultrasonics and microwaves; they fill an enclosure with radiation (which is why they are sometimes also refered to as volumetric systems). Thus all parts of the area are protected unless shielded by some structure or object which is opaque to the radiation used. As an enclosure is essential, they can only be used for indoor applications.

Ultrasonics are extremely vulnerable to false alarms due to air disturbances. These can be caused by many factors, i.e. draughts, air conditioning, ventilation, heating systems, as well as down-draughts from windows, and this is a major disadvantage. Added to these is the effect of harmonics from high-pitched sounds which can also affect the system. As a result of this some security system advisers do not recommend ultrasonic devices.

There are situations where ultrasonics can be useful such as a room or area where there are no draughts or heat differentials and preferably without windows, for example a strongroom or vault. One advantage is that, unlike microwaves, the radiation is confined to the required area and objects moving outside cannot trigger a false alarm (unless they generate ultrasonic sound). A disadvantage is that areas containing large objects or structural features such as a warehouse, or office with glass partitions could offer protection against ultrasonic detection to an intruder by their shielding effect.

Microwaves overcome some of the disadvantages of ultrasonic systems. They are not affected by air disturbance and can penetrate glass, wood and other similar materials thus depriving an intruder of any shield from such objects or structures. Metal objects such as filing cabinets, steel shelving and large machinery could though act as shields and thus produce blind spots.

With both ultrasonic and microwave detectors, shielding effects can be minimised by ceiling-mounted units, but these give protection to only a limited floor area beneath. Much depends therefore, on the floor area to be protected and the height of the ceiling, as the higher it is the larger the area that will be covered. Factories or warehouses with high roofs are in most cases best protected by a ceiling unit as a wide relatively shadow-free area can be achieved.

The main problem with microwaves is penetration of the boundary walls, ceiling and floor to give false alarms from external moving objects. Sensitivity of the unit needs to be carefully adjusted to give protection to the boundaries but not beyond. Ceiling mounting is a great help as floor penetration is then the only major consideration, and if the area is on the ground floor, there is no problem. Even here, sensitivity must not be too great as reflections could penetrate the walls, but it is not so critical as with horizontally-mounted units.

Infra-red beam-breaking systems are virtually free of false alarms when installed indoors. Not being volumetric and thus covering every inch of the protected area they do not offer quite the same degree of protection as the others. If, for example, an entrance was made through a wall or ceiling the intruder may escape the beams projected across the conventional entry points, but would be detected, by either ultrasonic or microwave systems using the Doppler effect. This weakness can be overcome by zig-zagging the infra-red beams across the area by using mirrors in a manner that anyone entering would be almost certain to intercept one of them. These do not look like mirrors, but are housed in boxes with a light filter over the aperture so that they are indistinguishable from either a projector or receiver, or in fact a dummy unit.

When first installing the infra-red system accurate alignment is needed especially when mirrors are used. This can be done by using a visible light beam source such as a torch placed in front of the projector. Optical filters will have to be removed from receiver and mirrors for this setting up operation and replaced when it is completed. Doppler systems require no beam alignment but the microwave units need careful sensitivity adjustment.

Once they are operating little can be done to defeat any of these systems. The infra-red beam can be physically avoided if only a single beam is projected across an entrance and its position is known; this can be overcome by lacing and fitting a few dummy units around. The microwave unit could be suppressed by a metal deflector plate fitted during the non-operating time, but such tampering would be detected by a monitor unit if included in the system. It is difficult to mount a deflector to a ceiling unit unobserved and this, together with the previously mentioned advantages make, the ceiling-mounting arrangement worthy of consideration. A well-installed infra-red system cannot be tampered with or evaded, and has the advantage of being false-alarm resistant. It is therefore favoured by many security firms.

Outdoor applications

For outdoor application the choice is between the microwave and infrared beam-breaking systems. The infra-red beam can be bent by means of mirrors to encompass the four sides of a rectangular enclosure providing allowance is made for range reduction due to reflection losses. Thus a single projector and receiver can be located close to each other at one corner of the rectangle. This saves unit costs and wiring. A microwave system would need four transmitters and receivers, one pair for each side, and power and alarm circuit wiring would have to be taken to each corner.

The range of the most powerful infra-red projector is about twice that of the largest microwave transmitter which is a help where deflection around an enclosure is required. Maximum range is 1000 ft (300 m), but allowing for three reflections this drops to around 400 ft (122 m). This then is the maximum perimeter distance that can be covered by a single projector and receiver. For larger areas two would be required, a pair for each two adjacent sides. For the single reflection at the connecting corner, the range falls to 750 ft (229 m) for the two sides or a total of 1500 ft (460 m) for the two pairs around the complete perimeter. The beam widens at such ranges and so makes alignment comparatively easy.

The infra-red system is therefore more economical, but there is a snag. It could be affected by ice and snow forming over the unit faces thus considerable attenuating the beam intensity in the same way as visible light is reduced when ice forms over car headlamps. Some outdoor units have built-in thermostatically controlled heaters, but these are not included in mirror assemblies. Microwaves are much less affected by these factors. For locations where snow and ice is a possibility, heated infra-red units without mirrors, or microwave systems should be employed. The mirrored infra-red arrangement should be confined to more temperate climates. The effect of ice and snow over a mirror or unit would not neutralise the alarm though, but would give a false alarm by interrupting the beam.

Power requirements for the three systems are 50-100 mA for ultrasonic units, 50-100 mA for infra-red devices, and 150-250 mA for microwave transmitters, all at a nominal 12 V. The built-in heater for the infra red outdoor unit requires an extra 250 mA.

False alarms due to beam interception by birds and other objects are countered in the microwave system by presetting the minimum area of an object that would trigger the alarm. In the case of the infrared installation, two parallel beams are required and this doubles the number of projectors and receivers needed. This could partially offset the economy of the system.

Other systems

There are other systems that use a form of energy as a sensor although these are much less common than the three already described. One of these is the *electrostatic* system. This uses the same principle as occasionally seen in some shop window advertising displays. In these a working model is connected to an electrode stuck on the inside of the shop window. Placing a finger over the electrode on the outside of the window introduces a capacitance to earth, as the human body is virtually an earthed mass. This capacitance affects a delicately balanced electronic circuit which trips a relay and switches on the model.

In the case of the alarm, an electrostatic field is generated around the sensor. Any mass introduced within the field upsets the balance and the associated electronic circuit triggers the alarm. The range of the device is limited to a few feet and so it woulf be used to protect a small area such as a doorway or window, or the immediate vicinity of a safe.

Another system is the radio-controlled alarm. The sensors are conventional switches which are fitted to doors and windows, but instead of being wired to the control unit, each sensor has a tiny radio transmitter powered by its own internal battery. When the sensor is operated, a radio signal is transmitted which is picked up by the control unit which then latches on an alarm in the usual way. The manufacturers state that a feature of the system is that it is portable, having no wiring and can be taken away if one moves house. To this end the sensors need not be screwed to the doors but can just be fixed with adhesive tape! In addition, being a radio transmitter, an annual licence is required to operate it. The system costs about four times more than a wired system but with fewer sensors included. Extra sensors can be obtained at extra cost.

While the system may appear to have little to commend it for normal use, there are certain commercial applications where it could offer positive advantages. Where valuable goods have to be moved around in a limited though relatively unprotected area such as goods yards, the trucks could be equipped with radio sensors with a key or secret means of cancelling for use of authorised personnel. Any attempt at hi-jacking or theft while unattended would sound either the main alarm or a special warning device in the security office.

Another useful feature of the radio system is the provision of radio panic buttons. Here again the application would be on large premises where valuables were stored or high security was necessary, and there was a possibility of personal attack. Such an attack may occur when the victim is out of reach of an installed panic button, but if he has a radio button in his pocket he can sound the alarm from any location within range. The range is about 200 ft (70 m) and the units will work from inside a pocket or handbag.

Conclusion

All the active devices described in this chapter, with the exception of outdoor microwave and infra-red perimeter guard beams, are designed to protect internal space areas. It is best of course that intruders do not gain access to the area, so the beam systems are no substitute for conventional sensors on all possible entry points. The systems are, however, valuable as a back-up system, or where it is impracticable to provide adequate protection by other means.

As previously mentioned beams are necessarily more complex than the simple reed, vibration or inertia sensor. The simplest systems are often the best providing they are effective. When choosing a system the situation should therefore be very carefully considered taking into account the layout of the premises, its use and possible entry points together with the various features of the available alarm systems, before deciding in favour of a particular type.

7

Sounding the Alarm

The majority of alarm systems employ some audible device to literally 'sound the alarm', and it follows that to achieve the urgency and to be heard over a wide area, the sound must be loud. As the whole alarm system culminates in the sounding device it means that this is at high risk from tampering, as if it is de-activated the complete installation is neutralised. Both these factors must be taken into account when selecting and installing the warning unit.

While many systems operate off the mains, batteries are used as a standby in case of mains failure. So for optimum security, the system must be designed to work satisfactorily from the standby batteries and this means limiting the current of the warning device to a value that can be sustained by the batteries for at least half an hour before polarising.

Sound levels and loudness

The sound level in decibels (dB) generated by a warning device needs to be of a high order, and this is often specified in maker's literature.

The human ear does not respond in a linear manner to increases in sound pressure, instead it follows a logarithmic law. This feature enables the ear to cope with a wide range of sound levels from a nearby clap of thunder to a leaf rustling. The dB ratio is therefore also logarithmic in nature. Some common values are:

$$6 \text{ dB} = \times 2;$$
$$10 \text{ dB} = \times 3;$$
$$12 \text{ dB} = \times 4;$$
$$18 \text{ dB} = \times 8;$$
$$20 \text{ dB} = \times 10$$

As the above are ratios, they must be related to something. Therefore when applied to sound pressure levels (SPL), it has reference to the threshold of human hearing which is taken as 0.0002 microbars. This is therefore the 0 dB level.

To give some practical meaning to the quoted figures, a few examples will be of assistance. The inside of a room in a quiet neighbourhood where there seems to be apparent 'silence' will have an SPL of around 20 dB, a quiet watch ticking about 30 dB. A whisper at a distance of 1 m is roughly 45 dB while a good speaking voice gives an average of 70 dB at the same distance. A vacuum cleaner clocks 75 dB at 1 m.

Anything over 80 dB is usually termed loud, while 100 dB is unpleasantly so. A pneumatic drill at 1 m generates 105-110 dB, while amplified sound at disco's is about the same level. This level of noise if sustained for a long period can produce ear damage. The threshold of pain is reached at 130 dB.

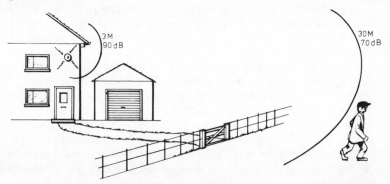

Figure 7.1 Sound decreases with distance. A bell giving 90 dB at 3 m will produce only 70 dB at 30 m. 90 dB is loud but no-one will hear it at 30 m

A point to note is that the sound pressure decreases with distance from the source (see *Figure 7.1*). It does this logarithmically, but if decibel notation is used we can calculate according to the values previously mentioned. Thus, at twice the distance, the level is 6 dB less, at three times the distance, 10 dB less and so on. Most warning devices are rated at a distance of 10 ft (3 m), but some less noisy ones have a rating at 3 ft (1 m). This can be deceptive if the distance is not taken into account. As the distance factor between the two ratings is three times, it means a 10 dB sound level difference. So, 80 dB at 10 ft is equivalent to 90 dB at 3 ft.

This also means that the sound level at the nearest point it is likely to be heard will be correspondingly less. For a device fitted at weatherboard level in a two-storey house this is about 15 ft (5 m) above the head of someone standing underneath. The 10 ft (3 m) sound level will therefore be decreased by about 5 dB. However, the nearest neighbour or passer-by is unlikely to be right underneath, but possibly quite a distance away. The sound level heard is thus further reduced.

For a detached building the distance may cause a drastic reduction in sound level. At 90 ft (30 m) for example, the level of a 90 dB device measured at 10 ft (3 m) will drop to 70 dB. This is audible but well below the sensation regarded as loud. Some increase on these figures can be expected due to reflection and reinforcement from the building itself.

Loudness of the warning signal usually means a high current as obviously more power is required to produce it. So, we have a conflict in requirements, low current is desirable for long battery life, yet a loud warning is required. When selecting a warning device then, both these aspects must be taken into consideration. The usual result is a compromise, but individual circumstances may warrant a weighing of one factor against the other. For large premises or those remote from the nearest road or habitation, loudness would be of paramount importance, and special arrangements may have to be made for adequate power supply. On the other hand for a terraced house with neighbours on either side and a short front garden, loudness would be a less vital factor.

One alarm system takes this problem into account. It can be powered from either mains or battery, and while the alarm in the battery mode is adequate for most purposes, an extra boost is given on mains. Consumption is low enough for permanent battery operation if desired, but if extra loudness is required the unit can be run from the mains. Batteries are required as a standby in the event of mains failure, and switch-over is automatic.

Bells

The most common warning device is the bell. The operating principle is simple, current is applied to a coil and a plunger is magnetically attracted through the centre to strike the rim of a bell dome (see *Figure 7.2*). As it does so, a pair of contacts is separated, and the current through the coil is interrupted. The plunger is returned to its rest position by means of a spring, the contacts close and the current is re-applied. The current thus flows in pulses which means that the average value is less than the instantaneous value of the pulse. The average depends on the ratio of the time the current is flowing to the time it is off.

The distance the plunger travels governs the quality of the ring. If it is too close to the dome one ring is dampened by the striker returning from the next and the result is a clattering rather than a ringing sound. If the plunger is too far away, it does not hit the dome with the full force and the individual strokes are too far apart in time; hence the sound is weak. There is then an optimum distance, which can be set by a screw adjustment of the contacts, or rotating the slightly eccentric dome. The older type of bell had the striker mounted on an arm and

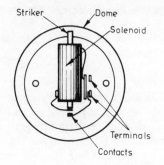

Figure 7.2 Basic principle of underdome bell. When solenoid is energised, striker is drawn upward hitting the dome. Contacts are also parted thus de-energising the solenoid and allowing striker to return to original position for the next stroke

the mechanism and coil located adjacent to the dome. Modern bells and, especially those used for alarm work, have everything concealed inside the dome.

Bells with current interruptor contacts will work on either direct or alternating current because current polarity does not affect the action of the striker. Thus they can be used either from a transformer powered from the mains or from a battery. Some bells are designed to work from a.c. only, and in these cases, contacts are not necessary. Thus a possible reliability hazard is eliminated, but there is no way that standby batteries can be used. For this reason bells operated by a.c. are not often employed as the sole sounding device for alarm circuits.

The standard alarm system voltage is 12 V and most bells are rated for this. Other voltages are available, these being 6 V, 24 V and 48 V, as well mains voltage types operating at 200-240 V. Voltage ratings are not critical and many bells are rated over a range of voltages such as 6-12 V, 12-24 V, etc. With such ratings, two current and sound pressure values are also given, each corresponding to the upper and lower voltage limit. Thus one bell with a 6-12 V rating has a current rating of 0.18-0.32 A, the higher current flowing when the highest voltage is applied. The SPL is given as 81-84 dB.

Another 6-12 V bell of a different make has a current rating of 0.18-0.2 A, and an SPL of 88-92 dB. This illustrates the point made previously about differences of efficiency, here a lower current at 12 V produces a louder sound than the other bell.

A bell used on the higher voltage of its range will draw a heavier current, but when a bell has been designed for a higher range the current will be less. Thus in the case of the first type of bell, the unit is available in several voltage ranges, the 12-24 V takes from 0.09-0.18 A, and the

24-48 V is rated from 0.05-0.09 A. Bells designed for mains voltage operation take a current of around 0.04A, and the sound output is usually higher than for low voltage bells. As the total power taken by the bell is about 9 W compared to the 2-4 W of the low voltage units, this is understandable. Mains voltage operation is not recommended as there is then no battery standby.

Enclosed bells

It has become the practice to enclose the bell in a metal or fibre glass case. This has two objects, to protect the bell from the weather, and also from tampering. To increase security many cases are fitted with anti-tamper microswitches which are connected to 24-hour circuits in the control unit, and therefore are always activated. Where the bell is mounted in a position that affords easy access it may be useful to enclose it. Even so, it can still be silenced by using plastic foam. An open

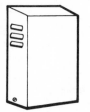 

Figure 7.3 (left) Steel bell box with side louvres. (right) Totally enclosed fibre-glass bell box

bell can prove more difficult. Inevitably, enclosing the bell reduces the radiated sound, and some fibre-glass cases which have no vents to prevent foam treatment, reduce it still more. The best protection is to mount the bell in a position where interference would be very difficult.

One argument against an open bell is that it can be silenced by simple removing the dome which is fixed by a single screw at its centre. Some bells however, use a special type of screw which needs a special tool to undo it. These afford an extra degree of security. As to the effects of weather, most bells are not weatherproofed and so should not be exposed to adverse conditions. A number of weatherproof models are available and these can be used without boxes for exterior applications.

The normal sized-dome for an alarm bell is 6 in (150 mm), but smaller ones, of 4 in (100 mm) diameter are used sometimes for interior work. Larger domes of 8 in (100 mm) and even 10 in (250 mm) diameter are available. As a general rule, the larger domes generate more volume of sound than smaller ones with the same mechanism. The difference varies;

it can be as much as 10 dB for a 2 in (50 mm) size difference, but 3-5 dB is more usual. One 10-in bell gives the same output as a 6 in model with the same mechanism, and the reason lies in the fact that mass plays just as important part as size. In this case, the 10 in dome is actually lighter than the 6 in. Large dome size and mass is therefore worthy of consideration where current economy and loudness are important factors.

Self-activating bells

The most vulnerable part of an alarm system is the wiring to the bell. In most cases if the *sensor* wiring is tampered with it will result in an alarm being sounded either immediately (if the system is switched on or the wiring is part of a 24-hour alert circuit), or the interference will be revealed when the alarm is switched on at night. If though the *bell* wiring is cut or short-circuited, the system is de-activated, and with most alarm systems this will not be discovered as the routine circuit tests do not include the bell circuit.

Unlike the sensor wiring which must be run in positions making it easy for would-be tamperers, the bell wiring has the advantage of a run which can be routed through generally inaccessible positions, in addition the wiring can be protected by metal conduit, and either buried in plaster, or under floorboards, etc. So, although vulnerable, it can be more readily protected, and if adequate protection is given the security risk is low.

Even so the wiring may represent the weak link in the chain, and if only an inch or two of wiring is exposed this would be sufficient for someone who had made it his business to familiarise himself with the

Figure 7.4 Self latching bell in box. Latching module and terminal strip can be seen, space is for housing internal batteries

system to put it out of action. For areas where a high degree of security is essential even this risk is unacceptable, and one answer is the self-activating bell. This is contained in a steel case together with a battery power supply and its own latching circuit (see *Figure 7.4*). It is thus independent of any external power and so is unaffected by any removal of power from the control unit. Having its own latching circuit means that it does not rely on the control panel even for this.

This type is controlled by means of an applied voltage which prevents the latching circuit from operating. The voltage is supplied by the control circuit of the system and is constantly present until a sensor is operated. When this happens the control panel removes the voltage and the self-activating latch switches on the bell. Subsequent re-application of the hold-off voltage does not switch off, so the alarm cannot be silenced from the control panel, it can only be stopped by re-setting the latch in the bell itself. If the bell is mounted in a normally inaccessible position (as it should be) this gives a high degree of security.

However, false alarms can be more than a nuisance as the very inaccessibility which provides security also makes it very difficult to switch off. If false alarms were frequent this could be a security hazard because each alarm would likely be of a considerable duration until it could be silenced. This could then lead to outsiders ignoring the real alarm. Great care must therefore be exercised to prevent false alarms if self-latching bells are in use.

If any attempt is made to tamper with the wiring by either cutting or short-circuiting, the hold-off voltage is removed and the alarm will sound. Thus a high degree of protection is achieved. It should be noted though that the security is not absolute as it is possible to defeat the system by bridging a battery across the bell wiring then cutting the wires. Thus the hold-off voltage is maintained by the connected battery and the bell prevented from sounding.

The polarity of the battery must be the same as that of the hold-off voltage from the control panel because both are in parallel before the bell wire is cut. Should the polarity be opposite, the two voltages will cancel and the latch will operate thereby sounding the alarm. There is then an even chance of a bridging battery either defeating the system or sounding the alarm depending on the way in which it is connected. It is not difficult though for a knowledgeable intruder to test the polarity before applying the bridging battery.

One way of making the system defeat-proof would be to use an oscillator in the control panel to generate an a.c. hold-off voltage of one particular frequency. Frequency selective circuits in the bell would respond only to that frequency. Any other frequency or a d.c. voltage would fail to hold off the latching circuit thus making tampering virtually impossible. A similar principle is used with infra-red detectors where the beam is modulated and the receiver detects only modulated rays thereby eliminating interference from steady infra-red sources. At present no self-latching bells are known that operate on this principle.

While self-latching units offer a degree of extra security over normal units they are not foolproof and furthermore they do have disadvantages. Apart from the false-alarm problem there are the internal batteries which must be supplied, checked occasionally and replaced, and the 24-hour hold-off voltage must be applied to stop the bell operating. The voltage must therefore be maintained even when the system is not in use and switched off, special provision being made for this in the control unit. Current must be supplied which may be modest with transistor latching circuits but could be heavy in the case of the simple relay latch.

The best protection for the bell wiring is complete concealment along the length of the run. This can be supplemented by a visible decoy wiring which can either be left unconnected as a dummy, or connected to a 24-hour loop. Thus any attempt at sabotage would be instantly detected. By this means the inconveniences of the self-latching bells are avoided without sacrifice of security.

Sirens

Where extra loud warnings are required or they must sound over much larger distances than usual, the siren will meet these conditions. This consists of an electric motor driving an impeller which forces air through vents in the casing in such a way as to produce a loud tone, usually of a raucous nature which serves to arrest attention. The complete unit is

Figure 7.5 (left) High power horizontal siren. (right) Smaller vertically mounted siren

totally enclosed and mostly is designed for outdoor application although smaller non-weatherproofed units are available for indoor use (see *Figure 7.5*).

Decibel ratings range from 90-110 dB at 3 m, the higher value being very loud, louder than a pneumatic drill! Makers usually give the range over which the siren is audible, but there is often inconsistency in the figures quoted. As the sound pressure level in dB's is inversely proportional to the distance, the range should be determinable from the given SPL at 3 m. Thus 110 dB SPL at 3 m, falls to 70 dB at 300 m, 60 dB at 1800 m. A 100 dB SPL decreases to a third of these values at the same distances, or the same values at a third of the distance, so the 60 dB level would be at 300 m. It all depends on the degree of sound level which is considered 'audible'. A whisper at 1 m is about 45 dB, but this would hardly be any use for an alarm.

The range of sound quoted usually assumes that the intervening air is still and at a uniform temperature. Even a slight breeze will make a considerable difference, increasing the range in the direction to which the breeze is blowing and decreasing it in all others. When the temperature of the air lying just above the ground is different from that above it, which is often the case, *refraction* takes place. When the ground air is colder than the higher layer, the sound waves are bent towards the earth and so travel along its surface for a considerable distance, but when the ground air is warmer, the waves are bent upwards and lost at only a moderate distance from the source. Convection currents from the warm ground can also carry sound upwards.

There are then many factors governing the range, and most serve to limit rather than extend it. Ambient noise too will affect audibility at any given location. Range can be calculated on the basis of the 3 m dB rating, but the figure should then be reduced to give a conservative figure more likely with unfavourable propagation conditions.

The frequency of the note produced varies between models and also with applied voltages. A higher voltage gives a higher frequency tone as well as a louder sound. The usual frequency range is between 600-1500 Hz. The ear is not uniformly sensitive to all frequencies, the most sensitive region being between 2-4 kHz. However, as higher frequencies are more readily absorbed and suffer from other losses, the lower portion of the sensitive region is the best. Hence tones from 1.5-2 kHz give greater audibility and are most effective for alarm sirens.

Supply current

As may be expected the much higher sound output of the siren compared to the bell is not obtained without cost, and so the current taken is also greater. This can be from 0.5-3 A depending on the voltage. As with bells, voltage ratings are mostly 12 V, with 24 V, 48 V and 240 V models being also available. Likewise, current is less for the higher voltage ratings, but efficiency tends to be lower with the higher voltages. Thus for one typical model generating 110 dB, the current for the 12 V unit is 1.5 A or 18 W, while that for the 24 V unit is 1.0 A or 24 W; the 240 V mains model takes 0.14 A which is 33 W.

Special consideration must be given to power supply when using a siren, especially one of the higher current models. Mains operation will be necessary, but it is the standby batteries that present the problem. The larger high-power dry batteries will provide currents of around 1 A for a limited period but are not very economical. A rechargeable unit such as a car battery is the most practical solution, but as this will necessarily have to be mounted outside of the control unit, it is essential to ensure adequate protection (against tampering) of the battery and wires.

Some control panels have a switched mains outlet and this could be used to feed a 240 V siren, while the normal output supplies a bell in the usual way. Thus when mains are present, both bell and siren will sound but if the mains should fail, the bell will still operate from the internal control-unit batteries. Having two independent alarm devices from separate power sources gives added security, so this seems a good solution. Of course the bell on its own does not have the range of the siren so this would have to be considered if long range is essential.

An electric motor takes a much higher current when starting than when running at full speed. This current can be two or three times greater, and sometimes even more. An important point to watch, is that the relay contacts in the control unit are rated to switch currents of this magnitude. If not they could become burnt and make future operation uncertain.

Electronic sirens

As an alternative to the conventional motor driven siren there are electronic devices which consist of an oscillator, power amplifier and loudspeaker (*Figure 7.6*). The loudspeaker is the folded-horn re-entrant

Figure 7.6 Electronic sirens

type often used for outdoor public-address work. All the electronic circuitry is built-in to the loudspeaker casing. As with motor sirens, the output differs between models, ranging from 95 dB to 120 dB at 3 m.

Electronic tone generation has the advantage of being versatile. The waveform can be shaped to give a piercing sound rather like a shriek — one that can hardly be ignored! Also more than one tone can be produced. One model generates two tones of 600 Hz and 1500 Hz with oscillation taking place between them to give a yodelling effect.

Another model uses frequencies of 800 Hz and 1 kHz which alternate at ninety times a minute to give a warbling tone. In addition to this a steady 1 kHz note can be produced and also a 1 kHz tone pulsed ninety times a minute. Thus there is a choice of three effects, any of which can be selected by switching or by wiring different control circuits to the appropriate terminals. One tone could be used for an intruder alarm, a second tone for fire, and a third for some special purpose such as

sounding the finishing time in a factory. This unit is available in three
different voltage versions, 12 V, 24 V, and 48 V. The 24 V model has a
further facility whereby the sound level can be increased by about 4 dB
with an increase of current consumption.

Horns

The electric horn is another device which can be used for alarm purposes.
It has a very familiar application in the car, and this type of instrument,
running as it does from 12 V could in theory be employed in an alarm
circuit. It gives a loud and raucous sound which is a desirable feature for
any alarm sounding device, but there is a possible drawback in that
many cars are now fitted with alarm circuits which sound the horn if
any attempt is made to tamper with them. Thus if there are a number
of parked cars in the vicinity, there could be confusion as to the source
of the sound. Passers-by could naturally think that one of those was
the subject of the intrusion rather than a building.

The horn has a rather high current consumption which can run into
several amps — higher even than the siren. If operated continuously for
a period the horn will soon exhaust a car battery, so dry batteries would
very quickly be polarised. Care would have to be taken to ensure that
the current did not exceed the rating of the control-circuit relay contacts. Most horns are designed for intermittent operation and, if sounded
continuously for a period may overheat.

Therefore, the car horn is not really suitable for intruder-warning
purposes on premises. There are mains voltage horns which take pro-
portionately less current and are designed for buildings, but with these
there is the usual snag of no battery standby operation in the event of
mains failure.

Making the choice

From the above it can be seen that there is a variety of choice of warning
devices. Selection will depend on the circumstances. Some installers
feel that any device is preferable to a bell, the reason being that the bell
has become commonplace and is frequently heard sounding as a result
of testing or false alarms. Thus it has lost its impact and tends to be
ignored. To some extent this may be true, but a bell is still associated
in the minds of most people with an alarm, either burglar or fire; whereas
hooters, sirens and horns can have many associations.

The bell is economical and so can be run from dry batteries for a fair
period before polarising them. If well made it is reliable and gives a

loud enough sound for most applications. The bell is an adequate warning device unless there are certain special considerations, such as extra loudness, which need to be met. Certainly it is the most convenient for domestic alarm systems.

Visual indication

In addition to the audible device a visual alarm indication is often useful. One alarm system kit has a red lamp fitted to the bottom of the bell box which comes on when the bell is activated. The purpose of this is that if the alarm is raised during the hours of darkness, it may not be immediately obvious which building is affected, so the lamp indicates the source and guides assistance to the right place. This could be especially useful where several homes in a small area are fitted with alarm systems.

The difficulty is that such a lamp needs to be bright if it is to accomplish its purpose, which means drawing appreciable current from the power supply. Such a lamp could in fact take more current than the bell which if run on dry batteries only could seriously affect the battery life. If a low-powered lamp is used it may not be noticed, especially if there is other illumination present, such as street lamps.

A practical solution to the problem is provided by another system. Operation is from either mains or battery, but when the mains are used a separate pair of contacts on the latching relay switches in a pair of mains outlet terminals. These can be connected to a separate porch-lamp or wall bulkhead-fitting housing up to a 100 W mains lamp, or even an outside floodlight. This comes on when the alarm sounds and not only indicates the source of the alarm but could assist in identifying the fleeing intruders by providing illumination. Several lamps can be wired, inside and out as long as the contact ratings of the relay are not exceeded.

When operating on battery either from choice or as a result of mains failure, the supply is not available and the lights if fitted, do not come on. Thus there is no extra drain from the battery; all the current is reserved for the primary purpose which is sounding the alarm. Only if mains power is present is the lighting circuit which is secondary, activated.

The switched mains supply can be used instead to feed extra alarm sounding units such as a mains bell or siren as mentioned previously. This enables high-powered devices to be used from the mains but still provides a lower powered alarm from the battery if the mains fail. The facility is therefore a versatile one capable of more than one application. It can be used also to power other equipment such as a tape recorder with a recorded dog barking or police sirens; or motor-operated shutters in display cases containing valuables.

Police telephone signalling equipment

Instead of, or in addition to, sounding the alarm on the spot, it is possible to summon the police by means of a direct wire to the nearest police station. The object of this is to catch the intruders in the act rather than frighten them away.

There are two units in the system, a transmitter together with its power supply which is installed at the protected premises, and a receiver with its power supply at the police station. Connection between the two is by means of a permanent Post Office telephone line. The equipment must conform to Home Office specifications and be approved by the Post Office.

The receiver, which incidentally can only be installed with the approval of the Chief Constable of the district, consists of an indicator panel which can accept a number of lines from various premises. Each line has its own indicator lamp and also a buzzer which gives audible warning of trouble. A typical receiver is shown in *Figure 7.7*.

The transmitter can be triggered by any of the normal sensors and can be linked to a conventional alarm circuit. It is essential that security is maintained over the Post Office line which could be the most vulnerable part of the system. This could be cut or otherwise tampered with, so the system must be designed to warn of any such interference. In addition it is necessary to minimise false alarms which not only would be wasteful of police time but could draw their resources from other actual break-ins.

Therefore, it is necessary to have some method of distinguishing between alarms and line faults. While the latter need to be attended to as soon as possible to maintain security, a means of identifying the two conditions will obviously assist the police in the action they take. To enable this to be done, a typical system sends a pulsed signal continually down the line. Circuits in the receiver sense these pulses and they hold off the relays operating the alarm indicators. Should these pulses cease due to a cut or broken line or any malfunction of the system, the relay switches on and a lamp indicating 'fault' lights up together with the buzzer sounding.

Should one of the sensors in the protected building be actuated, the control circuit sends a d.c. voltage along the line in place of the pulses. This continues to hold the relay controlling the 'fault' indicator off, but it actuates another relay which switches on the 'alarm' indicator. Thus it can be determined by which lamp comes on whether a sensor has been operated or there is a fault.

As the object is to apprehend the intruders, there is little point in having an audible alarm on the premises which sounds as soon as a sensor is actuated, because this would frighten them off before the police had a chance to get there. For this reason alarm systems linked to police signalling equipment usually incorporate a delay whereby a short period elapses sufficient for the police to arrive and station themselves around the outside of the premises, before the bell or other

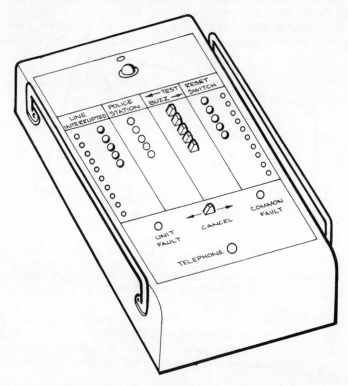

Figure 7.7 Direct police telephone signalling receiving panel. Installed in the police station, this will display either alarm or line fault conditions. Facilities for ten lines are included in this model but only five are in use. Unused sections are blanked off

audible alarm is sounded. When it does the intruders flee straight into the arms of the law. This eliminates the necessity of the police having to themselves enter the building and possibly lose the burglars in large or complicated premises. From the nature of the signals used to control the indicator it can be seen that it is very difficult to tamper with the line and defeat the alarm without actually operating the indicators at the receiving panel. A high degree of security is thereby afforded.

Automatic telephone dialling system

Another warning device of a similar nature to the Police signalling system is the automatic telephone dialler (*Figure 7.8*).

This automatically dials the required emergency service (it can be used for fire as well as police) and when the telephone at the receiving end is answered, a recorded message is delivered. The message is pre-recorded by the owner, and will be just a brief notification that there

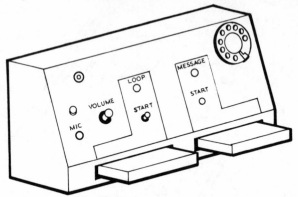

Figure 7.8 Telephone dialling unit. Recordings are made on the tape cartridges shown in front slots. In case of an alarm, the machine automatically dials the police and responsible staff members and delivers message

are intruders at the given address and that the message is recorded. The address, if not the complete message, should be repeated. After delivering the message to the police, further recorded messages can be sent to security or management personnel after dialling the appropriate home numbers.

Compared to the police signalling system there are advantages and disadvantages of the automatic dialler. The warning is not immediate, and as it relies on someone answering the phone, this could mean a delay especially if the local police station number was engaged. A 999 call may be safer, but part of the message may be lost while being connected to the appropriate service. A number of repeats is the best course. Another disadvantage is that the line is not protected against tampering to the extent of the signalling system. A fault triggers the internal alarm system but does not inform the police.

On the other hand, several messages can be sent to different numbers in addition to the police and thus responsible persons will be informed of events with little delay. Of course, the police would do this anyway on receipt of a warning signal from the other system.

The dialling system can be used where police permission to install direct signalling has been refused, as there is no special equipment to be set up in the police station. A special Post Office line does not have to be permanently connected to the dialler, so the line can be used during the day for normal telephone communication and switched to the dialler at night. Thus the individual circumstances determine the selection of the appropriate system together with the advantages which seem most beneficial.

Commercial detection stations

Where permission to use a direct signalling system is not granted yet the security of this type of installation is deemed essential, an alternative is to use one of the commercial detection stations operated by some of the alarm companies. Direct Post Office lines are installed beween the central station and all subscribers premises.

The equipment is similar to that used for direct police connection and the lines are continually monitored for faults or alarm conditions. When an alarm is received, the information is immediately communicated to the police.

This is somewhat different to the operation of such institutions in America where the alarm company's own security staff investigate any alarm.

Alarm combinations

It is often desirable to operate more than one alarm device from a common control cicrcuit. There are no major problems here but certain factors need to be considered. The main factor is the extra current and whether the system power supply can provide it for a reasonable period. When operated from the mains there is usually ample current, providing the system power transformers are adequately rated. The point to remember is that system may have to operate on the standby batteries. The addition of a siren to an exising bell or, even the substitution of one, would prove a serious drain on a battery which could not be sustained for long unless heavy duty rechargeable cells were used.

Even an extra bell of a high consumption type could result in excessive demands on the battery. Some models take 300 mA, so two bells would be a heavy drain. There are, however, models that take as little as 80 mA, and a pair, or even three of these could be easily supplied without difficulty.

Where an extra high output alarm device is required an ideal arrangement is that mentioned previously where a separate circuit is available for such from the control panel. This is only energised in the presence of the mains supply. So, if the mains are present as in most cases they will be, all is well and good, but should an alarm occur during a mains failure only one device will operate thus preserving the battery.

For most domestic and small business premises, it is a good practice to have two bells, the usual one on the exterior of the building and an extra one inside. In some situations, the external bell, normally fitted on the front of the building, may not readily be heard at the back or in some interior rooms. In particular it may not be heard by persons sleeping in the premises. For these and other reasons, the extra internal bell is desirable. A few systems supply one in the kit.

The extra bell can be a smaller unit than the main one, a 4 in (100 mm) type being usually adequate. In some larger premises such as hotels, garages and stores, a larger one may be preferable. The bell should be chosen for minimum current consumption as loudness is not quite so important as for the exterior bell. Even so, some bells combine low consumption with a good output and therefore are most suited for the purpose. Weatherproofing or enclosing is of course not necessary.

A point to be considered is the possible security hazard that could be presented by the internal bell. If intruders were bold enough to stay on premises for a short while with the alarm sounding, they could quickly find the internal bell by following the sound. (For this reason it should not be mounted near the control unit as they could thereby locate that too.) Having found the bell, it would be easy to silence it by removing the dome. Thus gaining access to the bell wire, a short-circuit placed across it will also short out the external bell as this is wired in parallel. Thus the whole system could be defeated in a matter of seconds. To avoid this, a 1 A fuse should always be wired in series with the internal bell at the control box.

It should be noted though, that the fuse itself can consistute a risk. A bad joint between the wire and the cartridge end-cap or poor contact in the fuse holder could put the internal bell out of action. For this reason a fuse should not be included in the circuit of the main exterior bell as it is unlikely that it would be tampered with in the same way.

8

Exits and Entrances

A basic problem which confronts anyone planning or installing an intruder alarm system is: how does the user leave the premises having switched the system on without setting off the alarm? Similarly, how does he re-enter again?

There are various methods whereby authorised persons can leave and enter a protected area without activating the alarm; each has advantages and disadvantages.

Bypass switches

A simple method is the use of a shunt switch which bypasses part of the loop connected to the sensor on the exit door. When the switch is closed, the sensor is short-circuited and the door can be opened without breaking the loop circuit. So that the switch can be opened and thus bring the exit-door sensor back into circuit after leaving, the switch must be situated on the outside of the protected area, or be operable from the outside. In the same way an entrance can be made by closing the switch from the outside.

The obvious snag with this arrangement is that an intruder may discover the switch, perhaps by observing the owner entering the premises, and so gain access himself. While he may subsequently be detected by other internal sensors, the degree of security is inevitably lessened. The situation is improved where the final exit door of the protected area is not an external door. Then the bypass switch can be concealed or disguised and as it would not be visible from outside of the premises the owner cannot be observed operating it.

A miniature switch can be concealed without much difficulty or it can be disguised as a light switch, for example it could be fitted on a double switch-plate alongside the real light switch. Another inconvenience with the use of a bypass switch is that it must always be in

the correct position before switching on the alarm system otherwise it
will sound as soon as the exit door is opened. Normally it would be
closed from the last entry and so in the right position for exit, but there
is a chance it might have been moved in the meantime.

*Figure 8.1 Key switch for mounting in exit
door*

These disadvantages can be overcome by using a key-operated switch
which can be mounted in the exit door (*Figure 8.1*). Thus security is
maintained even when the door is an exterior one, as only a key-holder
can operate the switch. Furthermore it would be unlikely to be left in
the wrong position subsequent to entry. The snag is that another key
must be added to what for most people is already an over-large collection,
the alarm control unit probably being already key-operated.

The lock switch

An alternative is the lock switch. This is high security mortice deadlock
that incorporates a microswitch. When the door is unlocked the switch
is closed thereby shunting the sensor, and when it is locked the switch
is opened thus removing the sensor shunt. The lock switch is one of the
best means of dealing with the exit and entry problem as it offers high
security, cannot be left in the wrong position to cause a false alarm, and
as the lock can take the place of an existing one, it does not call for an
extra key. If desired of course, the lock can be fitted as an extra to the
present lock, and although this means another key must be used, it
affords additional physical security.

In most locks the switch is a single pair of contacts intended to shunt
a normally-closed sensor. Some models have changeover switches which
enable them to be used either to shunt a normally-closed sensor, or to
open-circuit a normally-open sensor, or to do both where a high-security
four-wire or changeover sensor is fitted (*Figure 8.2*).

With either key switches or lock switches the wiring must be taken
from the door-frame to the door. Special loops are made for this purpose consisting of a number of insulated conductors each made of thin
flat copper-strip wire wound around a cord core. This gives extreme
flexibility, hence freedom from metal fatigue and breakage with frequent flexing. Loops are available with two, four or six conductors,

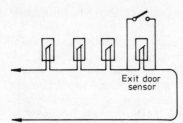

Exit door
sensor

Figure 8.2 By-pass switch connected across the sensor of the exit door. This can be either a key switch or lock switch

and have either bare ends or are fitted with junction boxes at each end. The conductors are enclosed in a further sheath of insulation, similar to an ordinary mains cable to give added physical protection. Surplus conductors could be used if required for a doorbell press.

Remote setting

Some control units have a facility whereby the whole system can be switched on from the exit-door key or lock switch. The simple shunt arrangements already described require the system to be first switched on from the control box, then for the exit door shunt to be operated when leaving. Likewise, the system must be switched off at the control box after switching on the door shunt when re-entering. Thus two operations are required for exit or entry, although where a lock switch is used, this is no more than one plus normal locking or unlocking operation.

There may be other sensors to be negotiated on the exit route from the control box such as doors and pressure mats, any of which should be accidentally set off. Each door on route would have to have its own shunt unless the exit door shunt served for them all. It can be seen then, that in some situations there can be complications. These can be overcome by remote setting.

Remote setting can be useful too where there are a number of key holders, not all of whom have a fully developed sense of responsibility. This could be the case with a club or meeting hall, where several members have keys for various activities and cleaning.

It is quite possible that an alarm system may be forgotten and left switched off, or there may be confusion as to its use and correct setting. A lock switch used to remotely set the system will overcome this problem as the installation will be automatically switched on each time the premises are locked up. This has an added advantage in that, if a protected door or window is left open, the alarm will sound thus drawing attention to the fact. In most cases, the lock will switch off the system completely so an exit alarm from this cause can be quickly silenced.

Some systems may have to be reset from the control box which obviously would cause some delay in silencing it.

Where the possibility of an exit false alarm is undesirable such as for premises used late in the evening in a residential area, a warning facility on the system is useful. In the case of one model if a sensor is open when the lock switches the system on, a buzzer sounds, but if a sensor is opened after the system is switched on, the normal alarm bell sounds. Thus, an exit false alarm just sounds the buzzer which cannot be heard at any distance and warns the keyholder that a protected door or window is open, but any subsequent opening by an intruder sounds the alarm.

In such circumstances, this arrangement is ideal, as the control panel need not be touched by those usually opening and shutting the premises; it could even be locked away in a cupboard. It is only necessary to ensure that all doors and windows are secured and that the main exit door is locked, nothing more in fact than would normally be expected, with the advantage that a warning is given if something *is* left open. However, someone should be made responsible for regularly testing the system from the control panel by the test facilities, if provided, or by sounding the actual alarm once in a while.

Delay loops

Another method of effecting an exit is the timed delay. There are many different arrangements but basically a separate loop facility is provided at the control box which if broken, does not immediately trigger the alarm. The loop is connected only to the exit door sensor so that an exit can be made within the delay time. After that, any operation of the sensor sounds the alarm.

Each variation has features which could be advantageous in certain circumstances. In one model, the delay can be set from between 1 to 4 min after switching on and the exit must be made within that time. As the sensor operates immediately after the delay has elapsed, subsequent entry sets off the alarm, so this means a false alarm each time the owner re-enters. A separate lamp which can be mounted in any convenient place comes on when the delay circuit is in operation and goes out when the delay has elapsed thus warning of its expiration.

Another model sounds a buzzer when switched on until the exit door sensor has been closed. A delay of 30 sec is allowed for this, after which the system switches over to the bell. If the 30 sec expires without the exit door being operated the alarm will sound. This gives a protection against personal attack on the way out and is a useful feature for business premises needing high secuity such as a jewellers.

A 30 sec delay is used in another model but with different results. After switching on, the whole system is alert except for the exit door which should be used within 30 sec. After this time, the alarm will be triggered if the door is opened, but the bell will not sound for a further 30 sec. This enables the owner to re-enter and switch off the alarm before the bell sounds.

Re-entry is a problem, as in some systems there is no provision for this at all and the alarm is sounded. With other systems a limited time is given to get to the control unit and switch off. This could easily be exceeded for example if one was loaded with parcels, or could not find the control box key to switch off, or fumbled with the key because of cold fingers. Delays could also occur on the way out due to the telephone ringing or someone calling at the door.

One system has a rather different delay arrangement which overcomes some of these difficulties. It has an 8 sec delay of the exit door itself.

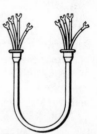

Figure 8.3 Four-core loop for connecting door switch to wiring on door frame. Wires consists of flat wire wound on cord for high flexibility

There is no limit to the time needed to get to the door after the system has been switched on, so there is no panic dash from the control box to the door. The delay starts from the time the door is opened and ends when it is shut. The 8 sec allowed although seemingly short, is just a comfortable time to open the door, pass through and shut it. When the door is shut, another 8 sec starts if it is re-opened, so if several people are leaving at short intervals, this can be done as long as each one shuts the door behind him. If the phone rings on the way out, it can be answered without switching off the alarm providing the exit door is closed. The same thing happens on re-entry, if the door is immediately closed there is no rush to get to the control box and shut it off.

Upstairs and downstairs

A complete domestic security system will include sensors fitted to doors and windows, both downstairs and upstairs. Thus, when on holiday or otherwise absent, the home will be fully protected against all possible means of entry. However, the upstairs protection may prove an inconvenience at night-time with windows having to be kept closed and visits to the bathroom likely to set off the alarm through internal door sensors.

The answer to this is to fit a shunt switch across that part of the loop feeding all the upstairs sensors. Being internal, within the protected area, it can be any convenient type of low-voltage switch, and can be left on as long as the family is in residence. When everyone is out it should be switched off thus activating the complete loop.

Where the premises are large, a similar arrangement can be made between the front and the back of the house. Many break-ins have been made at the back of the house while the family were watching television at the front. By such means the alarm system could be switched on protecting the rear of the premises, but leaving the front-room and front-door free.

Commercial entry devices

It is often necessary to permit only certain authoised persons to enter particular high-security parts of a building. One way of doing this is by means of an Entry Control Card System. This consists of an electrically controlled bolt which secures the entry door, and a card reader. The reader is a small steel case with a slot for inserting the card.

Cards have magnetic codes implanted in them and when placed in the reader, a switch is operated which energises the bolt allowing the door to be opened. When it is closed, the device resets. Unlike keys, cards cannot be duplicated, and should any fall into unauthorised hands, the reader can be altered to accept a new code.

Guarding fire exits

A security problem arises in the case of fire exits. These must be unlocked from the inside and so could provide an easy means of access from the outside. The standard panic-bar comprising a horizontal bar across the

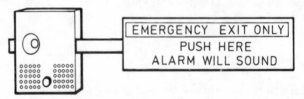

Figure 8.4 Exit alarm to prevent unauthorised use of exit doors without restricting emergency use

door which releases bolts at the top and bottom of the door prevents this, as the door is securely bolted yet it can be released by a forward push on the inside bar.

However, there is still the possibility that the door could be opened by an inside accomplice either to let in unauthorised persons or to pass goods outside. A device which overcomes this problem is the Emergency Exit Alarm. This is a strong security bolt fitted to a steel box which is mounted to the door. The bolt is released by a push-bar, but this also causes an alarm to sound. The alarm and supply battery are contained within the box, and so it is completely self-contained and independent of any other alarm system. A notice in large lettering appears on the push-bar warning that an alarm will sound, and so should deter any non-emergency use. Authorised personnel can bypass the alarm by using a key.

9

Closed Circuit Television

Closed-circuit television (CCTV) may be thought to be prohibitively expensive but the types used for surveillance work, especially the cameras, are much simplified compared to their broadcast studio counterparts, and give surprisingly good results. So the cost, although not cheap, is not prohibitive, and a basic system can compare favourable with many other types of property protection devices. Like any other system CCTV has its own features which make it more suitable for some applications than others.

Television is of course a highly technical medium, but the user of a CCTV system does not need to know all the technicalities involved. Familiarity with some of the basic principles though, can help decide whether it can be beneficially used in any given situation, and just how it can be applied.

The camera

Unlike studio cameras, CCTV surveillance units can be made quite small, hence can be unobtrusive in use. The heart of the camera is the tube which converts the picture focussed on to its target into an electrical signal. The larger the target area, the higher the picture definition, and for most CCTV work, the standard sizes are 30 mm, 25 mm (1 in); and 17 mm ($^2/_3$ in). For surveillance purposes the 17 mm size is quite adequate and is generally used.

The vidicon tube with an antimony trisulphide target is the standard unit giving good definition with low cost and reasonable sensitivity. Typical sensitivity range is from 2-20 lux which is the minimum light to give a viewable picture. Illumination level in bright sunlight is around 100 000 lux; at dusk it is about 100 lux; in bright moonlight 0.3 lux; half-moon 0.1 lux and starlight 0.001 lux. In well-lit towns the reflected light from the sky and clouds gives an ambient illumination of around

0.1 lux. Foot-candles are used in some specifications in place of lux. Conversion is simple; 1 foot candle is equal to 10 lux.

It can be seen that while in all levels of daylight illumination is more than adequate it is a different story at night and artificial lighting must be used to illuminate the viewing area. An alternative is to use one of several low-light camera tubes now available in place of the vidicon. The silicon-diode tube which uses an array of silicon diodes for the target, will operate down to 0.1-0.5 lux. It is especially sensitive in the infra-red region of the spectrum, so is particularly suitable for low-level illumination by incandescent electric lamps. Some other camera tubes using various types of target material are: Newvicon, Saticon and Chainicon. All work in low light levels, but the camera with a low light-level tube can cost two or three times as much as one with a standard vidicon.

Figure 9.1 Camera using a Newvicon low-light tube. This gives a high sensitivity with 600 lines resolution (National Panasonic)

Sensitivity is controlled by a pre-set adjustment on the camera which can be set for the amount of light present, thus in bright daylight sensitivity must be reduced. Some cameras have automatic sensitivity circuits which regulate it according to the light level. Light is also controlled by the lens aperture.

The electrical signal is produced by an electron beam scanning the target in a series of horizontal lines. A voltage is produced which is proportional to the amount of light falling on any given spot on the target, thus voltage variations appear which correspond to brightness fluctuations along the scanning line. Subsequent lines are traced beneath the first one until the bottom of the picture is reached whereupon the beam starts at the top of the picture again.

Each complete picture is made up of 625 lines, and there are 25 complete pictures every second. Actually the lines are not scanned consecutively, but all the odd numbers are scanned, then the even lines are scanned in between them. Thus there are two vertical scans for each picture giving 50 scans or frames per second. This *interlacing* as it is called, gives reduced flicker on the reproduced picture.

The beam is deflected horizontally along the line by an oscillator circuit that produces a saw-tooth waveform, that is one where the voltage rises linearly then drops suddenly to starting point at each cycle. At the end of each cycle which corresponds to the end of the line, a pulse is generated and added to the picture information. This synchronises a similar oscillator in the receiving set so that both oscillators run in step and the respective scanning lines start and end at the same time.

At the end of each frame, another longer pulse is inserted so that the vertical scan oscillator in the receiver keeps time with the one in the camera in the same way as does the line oscillator.

The exact speed or frequency of both line and frame oscillators can be varied by preset control in the camera, and when two or more cameras are to be used together, these must be adjusted so that they are as near to each other as possible. If this is not done the picture on the receiver, when switching from one camera to another, will go out of lock and slip either horizontally or vertically, or both. If it is required to mix or superimpose the pictures from two cameras, the sync pulses from one must be fed to the other so that the oscillators or *time-bases* as they are also termed, run at identical speed in both cameras.

Lenses

Cameras are usually supplied without lenses as there is an extensive range of these. Most lenses have a standard screw-in fitting which is known as the *C mount*. Different lenses are required for 25 mm and 17 mm tubes. These can be interchanged in some cases but will give a different focal length and may cause corner shadowing.

Lenses for surveillance work are usually of fixed focal length, although various values are obtainable. Small focal lengths give wide angle pictures, while large ones give close-ups with restricted field of view. Around 16 mm gives a good field of view, but if the camera is to be mounted at any distance, a higher value would be required. The lens includes a focus control which enables objects to be focused from infinity to a couple of feet.

Apertures for simple lenses are also fixed, from f 2.0 to f 1.4 being the usual range. The smaller the f-number the larger the aperture and the more light it will collect. It should be remembered that the price

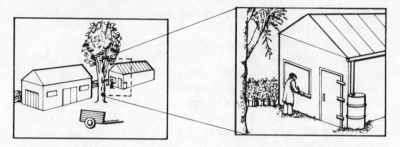

Figure 9.2 Wide-angle view for overall surveillance, with the actual effect of 6:1 zoom to examine any portion more closely. Zoom, as well as tilt-and-pan, can be remotely controlled

rises steeply with the larger ones of f1.0 and below. The sensitivity of a camera and its tube will depend on the aperture of the lens with which it is used.

Zoom lenses are fitted where a wide-angle view is required with the ability to close up for greater detail on any portion (see *Figure 9.2*). Each lens has a specified focal length range, a common one being 12.5-75 mm. This is a ratio of 6:1 which is the range of the zoom. Thus an object at maximum wide-angle setting will be magnified to 6 diameters large at maximum telephoto setting. Zoom ranges for CCTV run from 4:1 to 10:1. Most zoom lens have variable apertures, the quoted number being the largest, from which they usually stop down to about f5.6. All lenses other than the simplest are expensive and can cost several times the price of the camera.

Monitors

The monitor is the term used for the receiving set. It is similar to an ordinary television set but normally without the tuning and radio circuits. The incoming video signal from the camera is fed to a video amplifier which drives the cathode ray tube on which the picture is displayed (*Figure 9.3*). The synchronising pulses are separated and

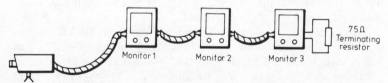

Figure 9.3 Video signal is conveyed to monitors via coaxial cable. Where more than one monitor is required, one must be looped from another, the final one being terminated with a 75-Ω resistor

applied to the horizontal and vertical time bases which produce deflection of the electron beam over the tube face.

A CCTV monitor is isolated from the mains supply by a power transformer, whereas a domestic TV receiver is not. If the monitor were not isolated, the connecting cable and the cameras could become live. Monitors are available in the same screen sizes as t.v. sets, from 9 in to 24 in. Although minus the tuning circuits, the mains isolation and generally more rugged construction makes the CCTV monitor rather more expensive than a similar sized TV set.

Distribution

The output from the camera is a video signal of approximately 1 V. It contains very high frequencies up to 5 mHz and so special connecting cable is necessary to convey the signal to the monitor. This is a co-axial cable with an inner conductor surrounded by copper braid screening, similar to TV aerial cable. Sometimes, double-screened cable is used to eliminate patterning effects on the picture caused by nearby radio transmitters.

Losses occur along the cable, but these are insignificant at normal distances. What is important is impedance matching. The impedance of the cable normally used is 75 Ω. Unlike cable resistance which is proportional to length, impedance does not change with length. This is fortunate as it greatly simplifies the matching. The output of the camera is of the same impedance and so perfectly matches the cable. It is essential that a load of the same impedance appears at the end of the line. Hence the monitor should have a 75 Ω resistor shunted across its input socket.

If more than one monitor is to be used, the cable should be looped from one to the other and not connected to a central point from which spurs run off to each monitor. Two sockets are provided on each monitor that are connected in parallel so that the cable from the camera is plugged into one and the cable to the next monitor is fitted to the other. A switch is provided which connects a 75 Ω resistor across the sockets, but this is switched off on every monitor except the final one, as the load must appear at the *end* of the line.

The function of this load resistor is to absorb all the energy sent down the cable. If it is omitted or of the wrong value, part of the signal will be reflected back along the line. This will arrive at the other monitors a fraction of a second later and will produce a ghost image displaced to the right of the main one. Sometimes the excess energy is reflected back and forth along the cable several times before it is absorbed, and each one produces a ghost image.

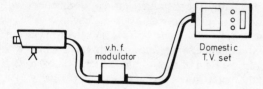

Figure 9.4 A uhf modulator can be used to convert the video signal to one similar to the normal broadcast services. An ordinary TV set can then be used as the receiver

Most CCTV systems distribute the video signal direct from the camera in this way, but a few use a uhf modulator (*Figure 9.4*). This is an inexpensive device which generates a carrier wave of the same frequency range as the broadcast television services. The video from the camera modulates the carrier, and the result can be fed into an ordinary television set using coaxial aerial cable. As second-hand TV receivers can be picked up quite cheaply, this makes for an inexpensive alternative to a video monitor. This is especially attractive if several sets are required. The receivers must be' of the 625-line standard, not the obsolete 405-line type.

The main disadvantage with uhf modulation is that losses over the cable are heavy which thereby cuts out long runs. For short distances though, the system is perfectly satisfactory, and if required several sets can be run by using uhf aerial splitters.

Watching a large area

If the area to be surveyed is greater than can be covered by a single fixed camera, there are two possibilities. The first is to use two or more cameras mounted in suitable positions. These can either be connected to individual monitors so that all the area can be viewed at the same time, or the outputs of the cameras can be switched to a single monitor.

Where several monitors are used, these will most conveniently be of a smaller screen size and grouped together so that all can be taken in at a glance. If desired, a single larger monitor could be included in the set-up and switching arranged so that any scene could be switched to the large screen if required.

Where a single monitor is employed costs will be considerably reduced but only one scene can be viewed at a time. With manual switching, frequent operation is needed to maintain constant vigilance. This could be tiring over a long period and human nature being what it is there would be a tendency for the observer to switch less and less frequently as time progressed thereby possibly missing something important. This can be overcome by the use of an automatic sequential switcher, which switches each camera in consecutively at time intervals. These intervals can be adjusted, usually from 2-30 sec and the camera can be stopped at any one if required. Some have an alarm mode whereby the operation of a sensor in the field of view of any camera will override the sequence switching and switch in the particular camera (*Figure 9.5*).

The alternative to having several cameras is to use one camera, strategically positioned, but with remote controlled pan-and-tilt head and possibly a remote controlled zoom lens. Panning is the horizontal camera movement and tilting describes the vertical. These functions can be performed by small built-in motors which are operated by controls from the monitor.

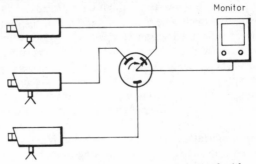

Figure 9.5 A number of cameras can be used with a single monitor by means of a sequential switcher. Each is connected in turn for up to 30 sec

This device would be used where only one general area is to be watched, even though it could be large. The lens would be kept on a wide-angle setting in order to observe the whole scene, or most of it, and a large-screen monitor would be needed so that small detail would not be missed. If required, any part of the picture can be zoomed up on with the precise portion being selected by operation of the pan-and-tilt controls.

In some situations, where the camera is mounted low down, the area where intruders may appear would be confined to a narrow horizontal view field. In such cases the panning facility only is required. For these situations camers with pan-only heads can be used, which are much cheaper than the pan-and-tilt variety.

Automatic surveillance

The basic requirement of the CCTV systems so far discussed is that there must be someone on hand to continually view the monitors. Human observation can be eliminated by automatic devices, such as the Motion Detector. With this device a number of points on the picture are selected by moveable small circles or rectangles which are electronically positioned at vulnerable spots. If any movement occurs in any one of these there will be a change in the video waveform at those points, and any such change will trigger an alarm. The device can thus be used without raising a false alarm where there may be movement at other points of the view such as trees moving in the wind or distant traffic.

Some units will trigger an alarm when movement occurs in much larger areas of the picture. This gives higher security but also the possibility of false alarms, unless used in situations such as indoors where there would be no random movement. A minimum size for moving objects can be set thereby eliminating birds and small animals. The alarm can either be the main intruder alarm, or an internal buzzer to alert nearby personnel.

A further refinement is the video recorder (*Figure 9.6*). It is sometimes useful to have a pictorial record of intruders in the act of entering, for evidence in court or identification. The main disadvantage with

Figure 9.6 Video recorder that will record up to 122 hours at low definition. If an intruder disturbs a sensor, or a motion detector senses a movement, the recorder speed is increased to give high-definition pictures

video recording is that tape is used up at a rapid rate. This is necessary to record the high frequencies present in the video signal. While the video tape can be re-recorded many thousands of times yet to make a good quality recording running for several hours such as overnight, or even longer over a weekend, the amount of tape required would be impractical.

One manufacturer has solved this problem by using a slow speed to make a low-definition recording of the scene while conditions are normal. If an intruder actuates an alarm sensor, the video recorder immediately steps up the tape speed to give a high-definition recording of the event.

By this means a 7 in spool of video tape will run for up to 122 hours, which is ample to cover the longest holiday weekend. The tape can be rewound in 9 min and, if there is an alarm and tape acceleration during recording, a red light comes on when the tape reaches that point while rewinding. Thus the spot can be located with a minimum of winding and rewinding.

Other facilities and features

Cameras intended for outdoor use can be provided with weatherproof housings, and there are housings for practically any environment. These include dustproof, heatproof, pressurised and even explosion-proof castings! Some are even designed for underwater use.

If detection is required in completely dark surroundings, this can be provided by the use of infra-red sensitive cameras and infra-red lamps. Another problem may be providing power for the camera which may be situated some way from a mains supply. Some systems are designed to supply the camera power from the monitor along the video cable.

It is possible to have the camera several miles distant from the monitor, perhaps in a different part of the city, including remote operation of pan tilt and zoom. One special Telemetry amplifier unit enables Post Office lines to be used for the purpose. Other amplifiers are available which allows a video signal to be sent along up to 3 miles of twin twisted flex.

A camera can be temporarily 'blinded' by car headlights, sun reflections or other powerful lights being directed into the lens. The automatic sensitivity circuit reacts to reduce the sensitivity, and thereby the rest of the picture goes dark leaving just the glare of the light. A device that prevents this is known as an Eclipser which effectively removes the highlights from a picture. Thus the reflection or headlamp appears black with just a halo of light while the rest of the picture is normal.

Applications of CCTV

Closed-circuit television is not suitable for all protection situations, but is ideal for others. Few domestic situations would warrant its use except perhaps in the case of large country houses. Wherever there are large rambling premises with outhouses, such as farms, market gardens timber yards and the like, CCTV may prove very useful to augment existing alarm systems or cover areas where conventional sensors could not give complete protection.

Security guards in factory premises have often been attacked when investigating an alarm. As a result, they have telephoned the police first on subsequent alarms only to find a large proportion were false, thus destroying the credibility of the alarm system. In such situations when CCTV is installed the problem is resolved as security staff can visually investigate any alarm without risk and then decide what action to take. Similarly security patrols can be dropped in favour of viewing the vulnerable areas from the safety of a central control point. Fewer security staff are necessary and the saving in wages would soon pay for the system.

CCTV is commonly used in stores to detect or deter shop-lifting. The deterrent effect is well-known, so much so that it is possible to obtain dummy cameras to install at various points. One point which is sometimes overlooked is the possibility of goods disappearing through the loading bays at the rear. A camera situated here could detect or deter such losses. This should not be a dummy, as it soon would become known among employees.

Cameras with vidicon tubes

Now for a general point on the use of cameras with vidicon tubes. The tube can be damaged by sunlight shining directly through the lens, so careful angling is necessary to avoid this possibility at any time of day. If the camera is aimed at the same scene for a protracted period, the scene will be permanently implanted on the tube target, and will appear in the background when used on other scenes. This 'ghost' scene becomes more noticeable when the new scene is dark or has dark portions.

When not in use a cover should be kept over the lens aperture, and if used with remote pan-and-tilt facilities, the position should be altered at each session. If the camera is on a fixed mounting, its position too could be slightly changed from time to time. The brighter the scene the more likely it is that it will be burnt on to the tube.

Flaring, that is the appearance of streamers behind moving objects also occurs with vidicon tubes and is more pronounced with dark scenes. This though is no great drawback for surveillance work where rapid movement, which produces the worst flaring, is rare.

10

Planning the System

The previous chapters have covered the details of the various parts of an alarm system and their advantages and disadvantages. We are now in a position to plan an effective system for any particular situation. The point made in chapter 1 that there is no such thing as absolute security should always be remembered. Given enough time and determination an intruder can gain entry almost anywhere. Therefore, protection is a matter of degree, and the first two questions to be answered are:

What degree of security do you need?
How much security equipment are you prepared to pay for?

Obviously domestic premises need less security than a jewellers or a bank because the would-be burglar is usually out for a quick and easy entry with minimum risk of detection, to pick up whatever may be of value. If one house looks as though it is going to be a lot of trouble, there are plenty of other houses that offer easier pickings. In the case of the jewel thief the rewards are much higher and greater effort and risk is accepted.

This does not mean that a householder can neglect any vulnerable point, the old adage 'that the strength of the chain is in its weakest link' applies. While the mere presence of an alarm bell will undoubtedly deter many intending intruders, some may be bold enough to try out a likely-looking entrance point, especially as an increasing number of bells, many of which are dummies, appear on homes.

Become a burglar!

Try to look at your premises through a burglar's eyes, put yourself in his shoes, take a walk around from the outside to see where you would break in if you had to. If you like, imagine you have locked yourself out and you have *got* to break in, but to save embarrassment you want to do it unobserved by the neighbours. One difference though, you are young, probably in your teens, and agile, so a little climbing about will be no obstacle.

Do not then overlook upstairs entries, especially if there is a nearby drainpipe, shed or outhouse, tree or other means of gaining access. *You* may have no head for heights but this probably does not apply to the burglar.

Intruders naturally like to be unobserved, and do not like a situation where they may be trapped, so a short exit path is highly desirable.

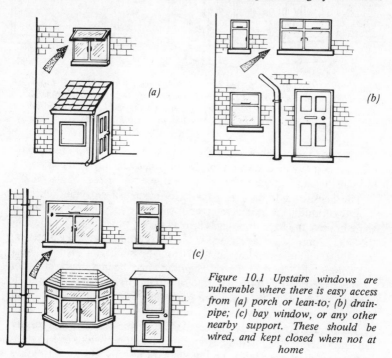

Figure 10.1 Upstairs windows are vulnerable where there is easy access from (a) porch or lean-to; (b) drain-pipe; (c) bay window, or any other nearby support. These should be wired, and kept closed when not at home

Break-ins at the rear of premises are therefore preferred, especially at houses that are detached, semi-detached or on the end of a row. Any cover afforded by trees or bushes is also very acceptable, and may tempt a break-in at the front. On the other hand house-fronts that are open, or near a busy street are much less vulnerable, and a nearby street lamp is a further deterrent.

Most exterior doors are obvious possibilities, but not all. A conservatory door, for example, seems an essential point to protect, but with so

much glass surrounding, the whole structure is vulnerable (*Figure 10.2*).
If the door is well-locked, the sheet of plastic roofing, which is commonly
used, could easily be removed. Protecting a conservatory is difficult,
and as little of value is kept there, is really pointless. As all conservatories

*Figure 10.2 It is hopeless to try to protect a conservatory, there is too much
glass, corrugated plastic roofing and a flimsy door. It is better to concentrate on
the conservatory door into the house (b). Fit a sensor and keep the door locked.
The same may apply to many built-out kitchens*

have a door into the house itself, this is the one to protect even though
it is not actually an exterior door. No intruder will stay in the conservatory, as the aim is to gain entry into the house.

The back or side door is a favourite means of entry and one that
should certainly be protected. Even here there may be exceptions. In
some houses, the back door leads into a kitchen which is built on beyond
the main house structure. There could be several other ways of getting
into the kitchen, a window being a strong possibility or even, although
less commonly, the roof. The kitchen then may be in a similar situation
to the conservatory, and therefore, although it is a good practice to
protect the back door, it is more important to protect the door from
the kitchen to the main part of the house.

The front door is usually protected although it is not always necessary.
Few intruders try to *force* the front door, it is too obvious and likely to
be the strongest door in the house; the back door is far more attractive.
Entries through front doors are sometimes made though, but usually by
means of a duplicate key, manipulating the lock or breaking a glass panel
and opening the lock by reaching through. Front doors containing glass
near the lock, or those with ordinary house locks should be protected,
but those without glass and fitted with security deadlocks need not be
wired unless a high degree of security is essential.

Remember that protected front doors give rise to the exit and entry
problems discussed in the last chapter, so if the door is secure much
inconvenience will be avoided by not wiring it. Of course, there is always

the 'peace-of-mind' factor, and misgivings may arise when away from home because of an unwired front door. It may then be as well to wire the door even if not strictly necessary.

Interior doors such as those into various rooms, are often omitted in any domestic alarm system. However, it is not at all a bad practice to wire certain doors. If an intruder should by some means gain entry without actuating one of the exterior sensors, he will almost certainly visit certain rooms, if not all. This will include the main bedroom, where there is likely to be jewellery, and the living room where there may be other valuables. If doors to these rooms are wired, the intruder

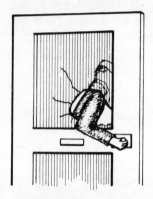

Figure 10.3 Glass-panelled front doors are extremely vulnerable especially if ordinary locks are fitted. Such doors should always be wired to the alarm. Solid wooden doors with security locks need not be wired as these are not likely to be attacked. All back doors into the main building should be wired

will inevitably be 'caught' by the alarm at those points. Interior doors are usually easy to wire and long cable runs are not involved, so they are well worth doing. A bypass switch will be needed for the bedroom so that a visit to the bathroom can be made without rousing the neighbourhood, the switch being inside the bedroom. If desired, it may be switched off during the night and only left on when away from home.

Windows

The major part of all break-ins involve entering through a window, so these must receive serious attention. Consider every window in the house and grade it, 'high risk', 'medium risk' or 'low risk'. All windows on the ground floor will be either high or medium risk, most being high Any windows that do not open are lower risk because entry would have to be made through a broken pane which means either removing every piece of glass or risking serious cuts.

The usual method of gaining access is to force a window open, or manipulate the catch from the outside which is a lot easier than it sounds. Where glazing and putty work is in poor condition entry has been made by removing it and lifting the glass out. Alternatively, the glass may be broken and the window catch operated to open the window.

All ground floor opening windows are therefore a high risk and should be protected. Easily-reached upstairs windows also must be considered vulnerable, especially those where a fly window is sometimes left open for ventilation as in a bathroom. This enables an adjacent window to be easily opened by using a loop of string, so either all fly windows should be kept shut, or the associated window should be wired.

Which are the best sensors for windows? For most applications the magnetic reed switch should be used; the choice being mainly between surface or flush-mounting units. The latter are less susceptible to damage, and are inconspicuous, but surface types may have to be used where the wooden frame is shallow or there is a metal frame.

Figure 10.4 Multiplicity of opening windows in a bay may prove a problem. A pressure mat under the carpet may be a more practical solution. To make sure, wire the room door as well

Most doors can be fitted with the flush type of sensor. Large areas of non-opening glass may be a problem, as although there are dangers in entering through smaller panes of glass, a hole could be made in a large one of sufficient size to allow access without too much risk. The metal window foil is the answer here, as its presence will be seen and recognised and therefore serve as a deterrent. Alternatively, vibration sensors can be used.

Bay windows can be a problem as there can be up to eight individual opening windows (*Figure 10.4*). Most bays have less than this, but even so a large number of sensors may have to be used to give full protection. An alternative is to place one or more pressure mats inside, in a position that an intruder would be certain to step on. Just to make sure, the door to that room could also be wired, as a burglar would certainly try to leave through the door to visit other rooms or establish an escape path.

It is not usually necessary to wire the small fly windows, as entry is not made through these, they are used to open the larger adjacent window, and this is the one to protect. However, in the case of clubs, meeting halls, canteens and the like, the fly windows themselves may be large enough to permit access. Furthermore, as these windows are often left open by careless key-holders, it may be advisable to have them all wired, then if an attempt is made to lock up and set the alarm with a window open, a warning will be given.

Roof entry

Although it is unusual for entry to be made through a roof it is a possibility which should be considered with a single-storey building, such as a bungalow or out-buildings. Where an increasing number of alarms are being fitted, most wired to the conventional entry points, burglars may be driven to seek other means of access that are not protected. It is comparatively easy to lift a few tiles and cut away any underfelt that may be fitted. With a bungalow protection can be readily obtained by fitting a sensor to the trap door giving access to the roof area.

In the case of single-storey industrial premises such as workshops, small factories, etc access could be made through the roof and a hole made in the ceiling which is likely to be of soft plasterboard. Thin wires stretched across the ceiling, supported by staples or by being papered over as described in an earlier chapter is probably the best, but again, vibration sensors or sonic sensors make suitable detectors and involve less work.

Having decided on the points to be protected and the type of sensor to be used, other parts of the system can now be planned. It is worth mentioning that free advice is available for domestic or industrial premises from the Crime Prevention Officer associated with the local police. He will inspect any premises and advise on where alarm sensors should be fitted and also on various points of physical security. This officer is not just a police officer that happens to be available at the time, but is specially trained for the job and his practised eye will often reveal weak and vulnerable areas that you may easily miss.

Locating the control box

The control box, being the heart of the system, is the next thing to consider. Particular requirements, such as exit and entry facilities, will help make a choice as to which system to use. The system can be delayed-setting or delayed-alarm, with a bypass key-switch or lock-switch on the exit door. If the exit door is the front door and this is not wired there may be no need for these facilities at all. Some control systems offer more than one type of exit facility.

Having decided on the system, the location of the control box must be determined. In some advertising literature it is often shown near the front door in full view. This is about the worst place, as an intruder could soon silence the alarm by attacking the box or cutting the bell wiring. Even if the wiring is buried in the wall, it would be torn away if the box were jemmied off the wall. A casual caller could observe the box and its wiring and so know exactly where to go and what to do when breaking in later.

The aim should be to conceal the box so that a search would be needed to find it. It would be most unlikely that an intruder would have the nerve to do this with the alarm sounding. Furthermore, the control should not be observable by casual callers. It certainly should not be in the entrance hall unless it can be concealed completely. Any room or cupboard can house it except perhaps the kitchen where steam and condensation could damage the circuit. Wherever it is planned to locate the control box, thought will have to be given to exit arrangements as the room door may be one it is decided to wire.

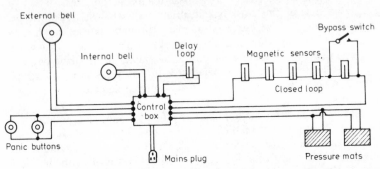

Figure 10.5 Complete wiring diagram of typical alarm system. This gives some idea of the number of wires coming back to the control box. It should be located to facilitate this wiring but in a concealed place

Another consideration is the wiring, all of which must be returned to the control box (*Figure 10.5*). Some situations may entail long or awkward runs. Remember that several sets of wiring are involved, the sensor loop, an open-circuit loop, (pressure mats, etc), a delay loop (if used), panic button circuit, mains supply (in many cases), and the bell wiring. Ideally, all this wiring should come in from different directions, otherwise there will be a conspicuous bunch of wires. The location of the control panel should facilitate easy wiring, and this is helped by using a fairly central situation for the installation.

The bell wiring should have particular attention as it is the most vulnerable. If this wiring is damaged the whole system is out of commission and most systems tests do not reveal it. A system that does test the bell circuit is therefore strongly recommended, and care taken to route the wiring where it cannot be damaged accidentally or deliberately. This is especially important in commercial or industrial premises where intended intruders may have previous access.

Where high security is required and there is the possibility of tampering, a dummy control box could be used. This could be mounted in a fairly conspicuous position with wiring running into it. The wiring must appear to be going somewhere, not just run for a yard or two then cut off. So it could be pushed down into a hole drilled in the floor and stapled or clipped into place, or fed into any likely-looking point where cables may be expected to run. Dummy boxes may be available from some alarm suppliers.

Alarm bells

The main bell must be mounted on the exterior of the building, in a position that is inaccessible except by using a ladder. This means high up, away from drainpipes, bay windows or other means which could afford access. The bell can be fixed vertically on the wall (most units are fitted this way) or horizontally under the eaves if room permits. The latter position is easier as it means screwing into wood instead of having to drill and plug a brick or stone wall. Also the wiring can be taken easily through the wood into the back of the bell.

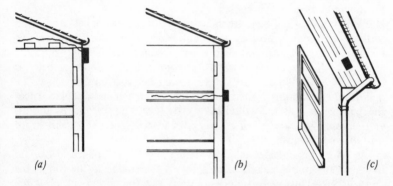

Figure 10.6 An outside bell can be fitted above room ceiling level then wiring can be run above ceiling to be dropped to where control box is located (a). If passing through an intervening storey it may be most convenient to take it down a corner or door frame. With 3-storey buildings (b) it is best to mount it between first and second floors. This is high enough to be beyond access, any higher would reduce sound volume at ground level. A good place is under the eaves (c) if they are wide enough. Fitting and drilling is easier, and wood can act as a sounding board

Wall mounting means making a hole right through from the inside, and this will influence the exact position as it would be undesirable for the wiring to come out in the middle of a room wall. It is best for it to terminate between ceiling and floorboards so that the cable can then be run under the floor and drop down through the ceiling immediately above the control box (*Figure 10.6*).

If the wall is stone or rough-cast, a flat surface such as a wooden base should be provided for mounting the bell, whether open or closed. This will prevent the ingress of moisture through any gaps at the rear, especially with open bells.

Another factor in locating the bell is that it must be in a position where it will be both seen and heard. This usually means fitting on the side of the house nearest the road, but not necessarily. The road may be little used, perhaps a cul-de-sac, yet there may be houses nearby, facing the side or rear of the premises. There is no point in putting the bell on a side of a building furthest from likely hearers. It should also be readily seen when approaching the premises from the normal entrance. As mentioned before, this in most cases will act as a deterrent and any thoughts of breaking and entering will end there.

If there is a conflict between these two requirements, or if the premises are extensive, two bells could be used, each on a different side of the building. In this case it is essential that low-consumption units are used otherwise the duration that standby batteries could sustain an alarm would be greatly curtailed.

While two exterior bells are not often used, an interior bell in addition to the outside one is more common and is a good practice. Some systems include an interior unit as standard. This would rouse sleeping occupants and scare off intruders who might have got in and actuated an interior sensor; the outside bell may not be readily heard from the inside. The bell should be mounted where it is difficult to reach and not placed near the control box as this could betray its location. A good position is at the top of the stair well as it is both inaccessible and can be heard upstairs and downstairs.

As with the outside bell, the wiring should be concealed over as much of the run as possible and a 1 A fuse included in the run at the control box. Thus any attempt to short out the wiring will blow the fuse and fail to silence the outside bell.

For industrial use, if it is considered that the bell wiring is vulnerable, a self-actuating bell may be used. This has the disadvantages described in chapter 7, so careful consideration must be given whether or not its use would be beneficial in any given circumstance. If at all possible it is better to fully protect the bell wiring over the whole of its run.

Panic buttons

These were described in chapter 3 and are valuable additions to the normal alarm system. An obvious place to install a panic button is near to the front door in case a caller tried to force his way into the house. However, if placed too close the intruder may push the householder backward beyond reach of the button before he or she realises what is happening. It would therefore be of more advantage to place the button a little way back in the hall.

It should not be installed in such a position where it could be accidentally set off, nor placed so that it would be difficult to reach in an emergency. These requirements are somewhat conflicting, and careful thought and perhaps a little experimenting should be tried with the button held in various positions before fixing. The button should also be out of reach to young children who may think it great fun to set off the alarm, but not beyond the reach of older children who may have cause to use it. At adult shoulder-height would seem to be the optimum elevation.

Another location where a panic button could be fitted is upstairs, perhaps in a bedroom. An intruder may break in during the day while the housewife is upstairs and unable to get to the control box or front-door panic button without a dangerous confrontation. Someone may be ill in bed or resting during the day when a entry is forced downstairs. A panic button near the bed would be invaluable in such circumstances, as of course these work without the system being switched on. Here again a location would have to be chosen that avoids the likelihood of false alarms.

Other places such as near the back door or elsewhere can also be provided with buttons, as there is no limit to the number that can be installed.

11

Protecting Business Premises

The information on planning an alarm system given in the last chapter which dealt principally with domestic installations also applies to business premises; there are though, certain special considerations which need to be taken into account. The protection achieved is a matter of degree, and the owner or manager will have to determined the amount of protection needed. A lot will depend on the nature of the business, a jeweller's shop will need much more protection than a grocery store, while protection for chemists and tobacconists would lie somewhere between.

A burglar is after small, valuable articles which are easily disposed of, but larger items will not be ignored if transport is available. The class of district will also have a bearing on the probability of a break-in.

External protection

As with domestic buildings, the first thing to do is to take a good look around the outside of the premises and note all the points where an entry would be possible. Remember that the burglar will have more time and be less likely to be disturbed when entering business premises at night or over a weekend than a private dwelling. The rewards are likely to be greater too than with private dwellings, so the effort at breaking in is likely to be more persistent.

All windows and doors into the main building should be wired, with special attention being given to those at the rear. Outhouses built on to the main premises need not be wired providing the entrance from them into the main building is protected. If anything of value is stored in the out-building, then of course they should be protected as well, although this may be difficult. It is safer though to keep valuable goods in the main building.

Entry through the roof is something to be considered, especially with low single-storey roofs, or ones where access is comparatively easy. Protection can be given by wiring a sensor to the roof-area trap door if there is one, by thin wires across the ceilings, or sonic and vibration detectors.

Shop windows can be protected by sonic vibration detectors or metal foil. However, in a case of smash-and-grab, the raiders make considerable noise by breaking the window which itself draws attention and so they have time only for a quick grab at a few small valuables. An alarm may seem therefore pointless, but it could prevent a longer stay to get a larger haul, and if there are visible signs that the window is wired to an alarm such as metal foil strips, it could act as a deterrent. If properly connected, foil will not generate false alarms as may the sonic or vibration sensor, so it really is the preferred method. All non-opening windows should be fitted with foil.

Internal tampering

With conventional shop premises, public access is limited to the shop itself, but with showrooms, offices and workshops, members of the public may be admitted on business. There could therefore be a possibility of tampering with the sensor loop, control box or other wiring.

The control panel should be beyond any region of legitimate access by outsiders and within the protected area. If considered vulnerable, a unit with tamper-proof case linked to a 24-hour loop should be chosen, then the alarm will sound if any attempt to tamper is made.

Bell wiring is particularly vital and should be buried or run in conduit so that it is inaccessible over the whole of its length. As for the sensor loop, this should be a four-wire circuit to confuse any would-be tamperers, and the colour coding of the wires should be changed around the circuit.

The diode sensors described in chapter 5 are worth considering as they give warning whenever there is any interference with the circuit, and so discovery of any trouble is not left to when the system is switched on before leaving. The sensors can only be used with the maker's own control box (Radiovisor), or one which enables the polarity of the loop to be reversed.

More elaborate protection

For large areas or those difficult to protect by conventional switch sensors, ultrasonic, infra-red or microwave detection may be necessary. The respective features of these were discussed in chapter 6 and will help to determine which is the most suitable in any particular situation. Infra-red detection has much to recommend it, especially its freedom from false alarms. Cost will obviously be a consideration.

Where merchandise is especially valuable and a high degree of security is required, or perhaps where the premises are remote from houses or other locations where an alarm bell could be heard, consideration should be given to a direct line to the police, or automatic dialling system. This is not cheap, but a worthwhile investment if the circumstances warrant it.

Closed-circuit television also has its uses, chiefly where security staff are available to maintain a visual check. Large or dangerous locations can be surveyed safely with a minimum of staff and even automatic surveillance can be carried out, with an alarm being given by moving objects in certain areas, and a recording being made of the incident. A basic system can be quite inexpensive, but the costs mount as refinements are added. Usually, CCTV is used to supplement a conventional alarm system. The appearance of TV cameras is in itself a deterrent.

Anti-theft alarms

So far we have described intruder alarm devices, that is equipment that will warn of the presence of an intruder in an area. Another problem arises in protecting goods in places where the public is freely admitted such as shops and showrooms. Shoplifting, as it is called, is probably the cause of greater losses to business than burglaries and break-ins, it being so widespread. Little can be done in the case of small low-cost items such as groceries, other than surveillance. CCTV is ideal for this in addition to store detectives.

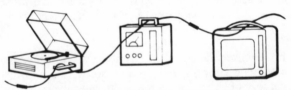

Figure 11.1 Wire loop threaded through handles or other projections of displayed merchandise. Small plugs and sockets (audio 2.5 or 3.5 mm jacks) enable items to be removed by the staff

Where there are larger valuable items, such as portable radios, tape recorders, cameras, etc an anti-theft loop can be employed. A single wire can be passed through handles, rings or other enclosed projections on the articles to form a complete loop back to the control box of an alarm system (*Figure 11.1*). The loop terminals can be brought out to some convenient point on a showcase or counter, and the actual loop wire connected to these. The loop can be broken at intervals by small in-line plugs and sockets, the 2.5 or 3.5 mm audio jack plug would be quite suitable for this. Thus, articles can be removed from the wire by an assistant easily, without unthreading and re-threading the whole loop, by simply unplugging the nearest connector.

A bypass switch can be fitted at some suitable point accessible only to the staff, such as behind the counter, so that the loop can be disconnected for demonstrating an item without sounding the alarm. The same loop can be wired through to several displays (*Figure 11.2*), but

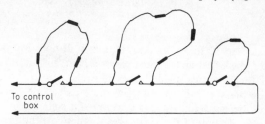

To control
box

Figure 11.2 Several displays can be served by the same loop, but each should have its own by-pass switch so that all are not deactivated when it is required to break any one

each display should have its own bypass switch so that all the others will be in operation when any one is disconnected. If this is not done, disconnecting one will leave all others unprotected. The switches should be operated unobtrusively, perhaps while looking for brochures, so that their location is not given away.

It is not desirable to have the main alarm bell sound in the event of an unauthorised disconnection of the loop as this could disturb other customers. During the day, the alarm system could be switched to something more discreet such as a buzzer which would alert the staff without creating a disturbance. Other parts of the alarm system, such as door sensors, would have to be switched out during the day and it could be arranged for a single double-pole switch to switch the buzzer and night sensors at a single operation. A better alternative is to have a completely separate system so that switching over, which may be forgotten, will be unnecessary.

Pressure mats can be used to warn of intrusion into prohibited areas such as a cashier's cubicle or behind the counter. These too can be controlled by a switch connected in series which can be set by staff during temporary absence.

Another use of pressure mats is to protect larger heavier goods displayed where they could be stolen, such as near the showroom door

(*Figure 11.3*). The items can be placed on the mats which function in the then normally closed-circuit mode and so can be wired in a loop. This is opposite to the usual mode of operation where the mat is normally open-circuit, and closes when someone steps on it. Thus if the article is removed, the mat goes open-circuit and the loop is broken.

Figure 11.3 A pressure mat wired in a loop (it is normally closed when article is in place) can be used to protect larger items. If placed under the leg of a display stand, the weight is concentrated in a smaller area and pressure is therefore greater. Otherwise weight may be insufficient to operate it

The pressure required to operate the mat is around 3 lb per square inch, thus the displayed goods must exert at least this pressure to close the loop. If the base area divided into the weight of the article is less than this the pressure will be insufficient. This can be overcome by using a small display stand such as a tripod and standing one or more feet on the mat. Owing to the small area of the feet, the pressure will be much greater. Hence, a tripod with an area of 1 sq. in. for each foot will have a total base area of 3 sq. in. and therefore an object of 10 lb will exert a pressure of 3.3 lb on each foot. Thus goods of this weight or more can be protected.

Figure 11.4 A display stand can be made consisting of a box with hinged lid. A microswitch supports the lid on its free side, and is depressed when displayed article is in place. When the article is removed, the switch is released. A by-pass switch at the rear or underneath enables staff to remove goods when required

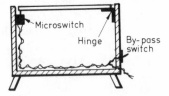

Another possibility for lighter objects is a display stand containing a microswitch beneath the display platform (*Figure 11.4*). The weight of any displayed goods depresses the platform which is hinged at one side, so that the microswitch is also depressed. If the goods are removed, the platform and switch are released. The platform itself will have to be light so that the microswitch is not depressed by its weight without any goods on it. A bypass switch at the rear can be unobtrusively operated by a sales assistant if the object needs to be removed for demonstration or sale.

For displayed electrical appliances a convenient alarm method is to fit all the mains leads with plugs which plug into special sockets wired in series to form a closed loop. The appliance must be switched on so that its internal circuit completes the loop. If any appliance is unplugged, the loop is thereby broken. Some equipment such as TV sets, may include a diode in the mains circuit, and so will only complete the circuit if wired one way. A marked plug with an internal link can be kept handy to replace any item temporarily removed for demonstration.

Personal attack

Personal attack is unfortunately an increasing hazard to staff having care of money or valuables. Even if not actually carried out, the threat of violence is made if the orders of the attacker are not complied with. A panic switch should therefore be installed where it can be operated without being observed. The most usual type is a foot switch. Unless the control unit has electronic latching, the switch should be self-latching with a key reset to prevent unauthorised cancellation.

Whether the full alarm will be sounded by operating the switch or a silent alarm elsewhere in the building will depend on circumstances. An audible alarm may endanger the staff concerned if the attacker has a firearm, whereas a silent warning could enable the police to be summoned and possibly arrive to catch him if he can be delayed by some means. On the other hand an audible alarm may scare off a less determined felon before anything is stolen or damaged.

Safes

Many business premises have some form of safe, and this is an obvious target for intruders. Where an alarm system is installed, it should be extended to include ths safe.

One of the several safe-sensors should be used, and in addition the area containing the safe should be provided with detectors such as pressure mats or an infra-red ray.

Hotels

A hotel can be one of the worst headaches from the security angle. It can be protected just as a private house during the off-season period, but when the season is in full swing, there are guests wandering in and out at all hours, and keys are handed out to all. There are likely to be valuables left in the guest's rooms, although a prudent hotel-keeper will warn against this. Really, a hotel can be a burglar's paradise!

Any conventional alarm system is likely to come unstuck with guests leaving bedroom windows open, and even perhaps opening lounge windows. The main danger is that of an intruder slipping in during the day while guests are out, or perhaps when at dinner and the staff are occupied. Most of the bedroom locks fitted in the majority of hotels would be child's play to an experienced burglar, but failing this, the use of a ladder and window-cleaner's outfit could easily disguise window entries.

One method suggests itself as a practical protection for guests be-belongings in the bedrooms. All bedroom locks could be ch•nged for lock switches which could only be locked from the outside. Internal bolts could be provided for the security of guests at night. The lock switch could be connected in series with one or two pressure pads near the window and dressing table, the whole lot being wired into a central alarm system, along with all the other bedrooms.

Thus when the door is locked, which means the guests are out, the pressure pads are on guard to trap anyone entering through the window or forcing the door without unlocking it. When the guests return the door is unlocked and the mats de-activated. As they cannot lock the door from the inside, they cannot themselves trigger the alarm by treading on activated mats. Indeed there is no need for them even to know that an alarm system is in operating in their bedroom, although some proprietors may choose to inform guests as an example of the care afforded them and their belongings by the establishment.

The wiring from each bedroom can be looped to that of the next, or a junction connection made so that a single pair of wires only run back to the control panel. As this circuit will have to be on guard at all times, either the system will have to be kept switched on, or if there are other sections such as in the private quarters, which must only be activated at night, a control unit with a 24-hour normally-open circuit facility will be required.

With larger premises having several floors, a unit having several inputs with indication of which one has been triggered could be useful to quickly identify the floor concerned.

Here again it may be considered desirable to have a buzzer operated in the private or staff quarters rather than an alarm bell which could disturb and cause consternation among other guests who might mistake it for a fire alarm. Investigation could then be conducted and the police telephoned, if required, without affecting anyone else.

In addition to intruders from outside, there is the possibility of guests straying into private areas, such as behind the bar. The proprietor should have some means of being warned of this, and pressure mats at strategic positions will serve the purpose. These need not, in fact should not, be wired to the main intruder system as this could cause confusion. It is better to have a simple battery operated buzzer with latching facility, in other words a very basic control unit. This can be switched on only when the staff are not on duty in the guest rooms.

Whilst many guests pay by cheque, care should be taken with the money storage as quite large sums can accumulate over the weekends. This should be adequately protect by sensors linked into the main system.

12

Installing the System

In the case of large commercial alarm systems, the best plan is probably to let one of the specialist security firms carry out the installation. They have the specialist knowledge and experience necessary, especially if infra-red, microwave, CCTV or automatic dialling systems are contemplated. The information so far presented in this book will enable an informed choice to be made of any options offered by such firms and the merits of alternative plans to be assessed. Cost of installation is recoverable against tax.

For the small business and, in particular, the domestic installation, there is no reason why the owner should not carry out the work himself. Money will certainly be saved by doing so, and the skills required are no more than needed for the average d.i.y. job around the home or shop.

The control box

The position of the various installation points including the control box will have been already decided according to the principles outlined in chapter 10. So, the first job can be to mount the box in its chosen position. If mounted on wood this means just screwing the unit through the holes provided in the back, but if on a stone or brick wall, the wall will have to be drilled and plugged.

If the unit requires a mains supply, then this must be provided. The simplest way is to run a cable from the nearest outlet socket, but this poses a security hazard. The socket could be switched off or the plug to the control box pulled out, or as sometimes happens the plug may be partially dislodged to give an intermittent contact. Provided the box is designed for it, the ideal way is to wire the mains directly to the house supply circuit without any intervening plugs or sockets. To enable this to be done safely, the control box should have a mains switch and fuses included. Alternatively, a special fused switch can be mounted along-side the unit and wired in.

No connection to the house wiring should be attempted by anyone not competent to do so, and it is preferable to have this part of the system installed by an electrician. If the system runs solely on batteries, then obviously there is no problem.

The bell

The first step in fixing the external bell is to drill the hole through the wall necessary for passing the cable. An extra long No. 10 masonry drill fitted to an electric drill is the best method (*Figure 12.1*). It is some-times possible to hire a complete drilling unit from a plant-hire firm.

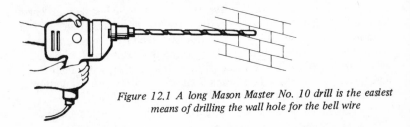

Figure 12.1 A long Mason Master No. 10 drill is the easiest means of drilling the wall hole for the bell wire

Alternatively the hole can be made with a long hammer-drill, but this is hard work.

As a general rule it is better to start the hole from the inside as usually precise location of the inside of the hole is more important than that of the outside. Also drilling in from the outside may dislodge an area of plaster or otherwise damage the decorations. If the hole is being brought out under the floor, then the start can be made from the outside as it may be difficult to drill from the inside. Accurate measurements will be necessary though to ensure the hole comes out in the desired place.

Now the bell-box base plate (or the bell itself if of the open variety) can be fixed. Unless the unit is to be mounted on wood, the wall must be drilled and plugged. These holes should be deep enough to allow at least 1 in (25 mm) of screw thread or longer if possible, to penetrate into the wall. Smear the screws with grease to inhibit rust. An open bell should have a rubber or plastic ring between it and the wall to prevent moisture entering. A very rough wall will need a wooden base on which to mount the bell, and this should be fixed to the wall by four or more screws having at least an inch of thread into the wall. Heads should be countersunk and puttied over.

Ordinary 5 A mains flex can be used for the bell wire. This is preferable to what is commonly known as 'bell wire' as it has a lower resistance and therefore does not waste power in the form of a voltage drop over the run. This is especially important if the run is a long one, although runs should always be kept as short as possible. If any difficulty is experienced in getting the wire through the hole in the wall, a piece of stiff wire pushed through first with the flex fastened to one end should do the trick.

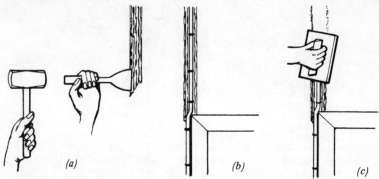

(a) (b) (c)

Figure 12.2 (a) For cable down-drops from the floor above cut a narrow channel in the plaster from ceiling to top of door-frame. (b) Clip cable into channel and continue down side of door frame to skirting. Door frame saves having to make a long channel down the plaster, but for maximum security bell wire should be buried in plaster all the way to the control box. (c) Finally, plaster over the wire

It is especially important when running the bell wire back to the control box to avoid anything which may constitute a hazard to it as the security of the whole system depends on this wire. Keep it out of the way and if possible bury it in plaster on the down-drop. This is not very difficult although it means spoiling the room decorations. A narrow channel can be cut in the plaster down the wall with a hammer and cold chisel. The wire is laid in it and secured with a few staples, then some plaster is mixed up and applied over the wire, and smoothed down with a trowel (*Figure 12.2*).

To pass the wire through a ceiling, a small hole can be made from underneath with a long screwdriver. This should be made right into the corner between wall and ceiling. A little plaster can be chipped away from the wall so that the hole actually starts below the surface of the wall (*Figure 12.3*). Thus, when the wire is laid down the channel cut in the plaster there will be no visible sign where the wire is run after the wall has been re-papered. When the ceiling hole is made with the screwdriver, push the tool into the hole up to the handle and leave it there. Then the blade can be seen under the floorboards upstairs, and so the hole is easily located. If the screwdriver is withdrawn when the hole is made, it may be difficult subsequently to find the other end of the hole.

The internal bell, if supplied, can now be fitted and the wire run back to the control box in a similar manner. Concealing the wire, although

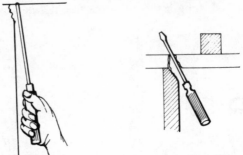

Figure 12.3 (left) A hole can be made in the ceiling with an old screwdriver. Chip a little plaster from the top of the wall so that the hole is below the level of the plaster. (right) If screwdriver is pushed in up to the handle, the blade will mark the other side of the hole which may otherwise be difficult to locate

desirable for the sake of appearance is not absolutely essential in a private home so long as it is reasonably safe from accidental damage and it is concealed at both ends, i.e. at the bell and at the control box. In business premises or where outsiders are admitted, the bell wire should be concealed over the whole of its run to achieve maximum security.

Sensor loop

Now comes what is probably the biggest part of the job, wiring the sensor loop. Single wire, not too thick, is needed for this and a rough measurement can be made of the total run with a good safety margin added so that sufficient wire is purchased. Some kit makers supply the loop wire which is sufficient for the average installation.

In most cases, the sensors will be magnetic reed switches with matching magnets. The switch is fixed to the opening side of a door or window frame, and the magnet to the door or window itself. Hence the wiring must be run so that it terminates at the opening side of the window or door to be protected. Remember that the circuit is a loop, so a single wire goes from the control box to the first sensor, from there to the next sensor and so on until finally the last wire comes from the final sensor back to the box. So, although two wires are run to each sensor they are only run together along the approach path to the sensor, after that they go their separate ways.

It is a good idea to make a wiring plan of the loop showing the sequence of the sensors and where any bypass switches must be included. This helps to avoid wiring errors. Where there are bypass switches, the wire from the previous sensor (unbypassed) should be taken to one terminal of the switch, and from the *same* terminal on to the sensor to be bypassed. The other wire from that sensor is returned to the opposite terminal of the switch, and from this terminal another wire is run to the next unbypassed sensor. Several sensors can be bypassed by the same switch if required by taking the last wire from the final sensor to be bypassed back to the opposite terminal of the switch, (see *Figure 12.4*).

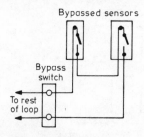

Figure 12.4 Wiring of bypass switch across sensor(s) to be switched out

There are two possible ways of running the loop, one by taking the wiring at floor level, along skirting boards, and the other above the ceiling under the floorboards of the storey above. The latter may be easier if there is not much furniture and carpeting to move and the floorboards come up easily. If the floorboards have to be raised for running the bell wire, it may be an idea to run the loop wiring at the same time. Otherwise, the skirting board run will have to be used; this actually is the most common method. If a loop has to serve sensors upstairs as well as downstairs, it may be that a single underfloor distribution will serve both, with wires being taken up or down according to sensor location on the two floors.

The main snag with the skirting board run is that of crossing doorways. The wiring either has to pass under the door space in some way (possible if there is a draught excluder fitted to the floor under which the wire can be run), or up over and down the doorframe. If a fitted carpet passes through the doorway, the wire can be run underneath as long as it is stapled at both sides. Note that mains wiring should never be run under carpets. The doorway problem is eliminated if the wiring is dropped from above (see *Figure 12.5*).

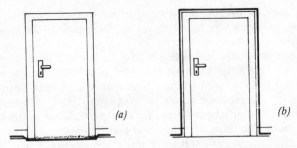

Figure 12.5 Crossing a door can be a problem. If there is a carpet extending through the door or a fixed draught excluder wiring can be taken underneath (a). If the floor is bare, wiring must be taken over the door frame (b)

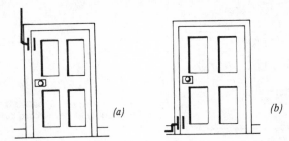

Figure 12.6 Position of sensors depends on the run of wiring if dropped from under the floor above (a) sensor can be near the top of the door; if run along the skirting (b), sensor can be low

The location of the sensor on the door or window is determined by which of these two wiring methods are used (*Figure 12.6*). If the wiring is taken around the skirting, the sensors will be low, near the bottom of the door, or the lower edge of the window, but if the wiring comes down from the ceiling, the sensors will be fitted to the upper part.

Fitting the sensors

Flush-mounting sensors should be used if at all possible. This means hollowing out the woodwork which is a little extra trouble but well worth it in terms of appearance and extra security. The sensor should be placed against the frame and a line drawn around it. Using a sharp chisel and mallet, this area can be removed to a depth of about 2 mm. Thus the flange of the sensor will be sunk into the wood so that the surface will be perfectly flush with the door frame.

Next, the area of the body must be marked out inside the 2 mm depression, and wood removed with the chisel from this area to a depth sufficient accomodate the body of the sensor, plus a little extra to take the wiring. If the sides of this hole are uneven or rough there is no need to worry as it will all be covered by the overlapping flange; it is the flange incision which should be accurate and neat (see *Figure 12.7*).

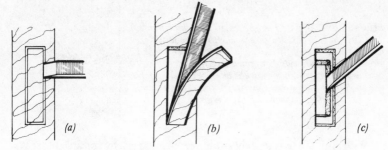

Figure 12.7 Cutting the door-frame to take a flush-mounted sensor. (a) Mark out sensor and make 2 mm deep cut with chisel. (b) Remove thin layer of wood. (c) Mark out smaller rectangle slightly larger than body of sensor, cut the marks and excavate the wood. Make cavity a little deeper than depth of sensor to accommodate surplus wiring

Now for the wires. A hole must be drilled from the bottom of the cavity, through the door frame out to the side so that the wire can pass right through the frame without being seen. The length of this hole may need to be longer than the size of the longest wood drills, especially if it has to be run on a slant. This can be achieved by drilling from both ends so that the two drillings meet.

This may sound very difficult, and indeed if drilled in a straight line hoping that the holes meet end to end, the chances are that they will miss. There are two practical tips which give a good chance of merging the holes, providing care is taken.

Firstly, both holes should be drilled at a slight downward angle so that they form a shallow V. This gives a limited tolerance to the vertical angle of the second hole; if drilled at slightly different angles it will still intersect with the first hole. The other tip is to drill the first hole with the largest drill, usually a $\frac{1}{4}$ inch, but the second hold should only be large enough to take the wire, $\frac{1}{8}$th or $\frac{5}{32}$nd. This can be done because the first hole is concealed whereas the second is visible and so needs to be neat. The larger first hole enables the second to be more easily 'find' it (see *Figure 12.8*).

The wires are fed in from the back through the smaller second hole and come out into the cavity. There they are cut to length in readiness for connecting to the sensor. Do not cut them too short, but allow a few inches extra. This will enable the sensor to be removed if necessary in the future; if the wires are pulled tight this will be impossible. The surplus wire can be accommodated at the bottom of the cavity which should be a little deeper than the depth of the sensor.

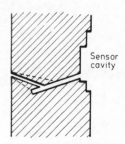

Figure 12.8 Making two holes meet in wide door-frame. The first hole from the sensor cavity is made with a large drill at a slightly downward angle. The second from the opposite side is of smaller bore, also slightly downward. Dotted lines show the angle tolerance. Hole can be drilled anywhere between these angles and still intersect with the first one

With some reed switches the connection is by means of screw terminals, but with others there are two thick wires coming from the glass capsule, and the circuit wires must be soldered to these. While screw terminals are more convenient, screws can become loose or the contacts oxidise, whereas soldered connections if properly made can last for ever. It is most important that all connections in the loop be above reproach. Should any one prove to be intermittent it will give rise to false alarms and there will be no means of telling the source.

If soldering is necessary, apply the iron to the sensor lead-out wires and then apply some solder to the wires, thus melting the solder directly onto the wire. It will flow over the surface to coat it whereupon the surface is said to be tinned. Do not try to apply the solder by running or smearing it on from the iron, the wire should be hot enough to melt the solder itself.

Tin the circuit wires in the same way and wrap them around the lead-out wires for a few turns. Finally, apply the iron to the joint until

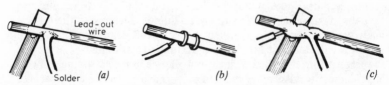

Figure 12.9 Soldering wiring to magnetic reed lead-out wire. (a) Heat the wire with the iron and apply solder to the wire so that it melts and runs easily over the surface, coating it. (b) After similarly coating (tinning) the circuit wire, wrap it around the lead-out wire a couple of times. (c) Heat once more with the iron and apply a little more solder. Solder should flow freely over the joint. Do not move the joint when cooling

the solder is melted and merges, and add a little extra. Do not let the wire move while the solder is solidifying. In most cases the sensor wires will be clean and will take the solder readily and likewise the freshly stripped circuit wire. However if the wires appear dull or discoloured or

(a)   (b)

Figure 12.10 (a) If wires are given a clockwise twist around a screw terminal, tightening will draw the wire in to the centre. (b) If an anticlockwise curl is made, tightening will push the wire out toward the edge where it may come away

the solder does not flow easily over the surface but remains in blobs on certain areas, then the wires should be cleaned by scraping or rubbing with an abrasive surface.

If screw terminals are fitted, the wire should be curled around clockwise under the screw head. This will draw the wire in as the screw is tightened, an anti-clockwise curl will tend to throw it out. Do not let the wire overlap on itself as it will be held then only at that point. Tighten well, but not to the point where screw thread may be stripped or the head twist off.

Figure 12.11 Surface mounted sensors screwed to door and frame

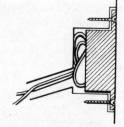

Having connected the sensor it now can be placed in the door-frame cavity, and screwed in by means of countersunk screws through holes in the flanges. Many sensors do not have holes provided in the flanges, so with these they will have to be drilled. Taper them with a countersink bit so that the screws will fit flush with the surface.

Now the magnet unit can be fitted into the edge of the door or window so that it lies adjacent to the sensor when closed. As the unit matches that of the reed switch, the wood excavation work is the same as for the door frame except that as there is no wiring no holes are required for it.

Finally, any gaps or other damage to the wood surface that is not covered by the flanges can be puttied in and the whole surface painted

over. It may be prudent though to leave this finishing off until after the
system has been completed and tested.

Surface sensors are much easier to fit as they are just screwed to the
surface of the frame and the door or window. The wire is then stapled
along the frame and no drilling is required. There can be a problem if
the door is recessed into the frame so that the door and frame surfaces
are not in line. It will be more satisfactory in such a case to use a flush-
fitting unit. Surface sensors are readily visible and so for appearance

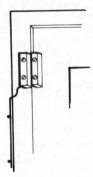

*Figure 12.12 Flush-sensor in position in cavity. Surplus
wire needed to enable withdrawal for future
examination is stored at bottom of cavity which should
be deep enough to accommodate it*

and security are less desirable than the flush mounting models. The
security aspect is worthy of special consideration where premises are
accessible to outsiders.

Surface sensors should only be used where the frame or door is too
shallow or narrow to accept the flush unit, or with metal windows where
there may be no alternative. Fixing may be a problem on metal; self-
tapping screws could be used, but these would most likely protrude on
the outside of the frame. The only thing to do here is to use an adhesive.
This should be quite satisfactory as the units are light and not subject
to any force.

Paint should be removed from the metal surface which should then
be cleaned and scored by scratching with a sharp implement. A good
contact adhesive should do the trick, but if the sensor is to be placed
where there could be a heat build-up such as a sunny window, epoxy
resin is better. Note though, that some types of plastic will not bond
to epoxy resin and this may be found with some plastic sensor-casings.

Pressure mats

These should nearly always be used under fitted carpet. If used under
small rugs or mats they may become displaced and so become visible.
Also it will be difficult to conceal the wiring which could actually
become a safety hazard as people could trip over it. A pair of wires is

brought out from the sealed mat, so the circuit wires must be connected to these.

As a block connector would cause a lump in the carpet, the wires must be twisted together. If at all possible it is best that the wires should be soldered, but if not a good joint must be made physically. Strip back the wires exposing about 2 in (50 mm) then tie two knots. Pull the wires so that the knots tighten then twist the surplus wire around the remaining exposed wire. Finally, bind some insulation tape around the joint. If a twist is made without knotting, the joint could pull apart.

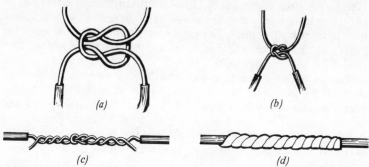

Figure 12.13 To join a wire without a terminal block such as for a pressure mat if soldering is not practicable. (a) Tie two kots to make a reef knot in the stripped wires. (b) Pull the knot tight. (c) Twist surplus wire back with exposed wire. (d) Insulate with tape

The wire can be laid back to emerge from the carpet at a convenient point for continuing the run back to the control box, usually the room door frame. Remember that pressure mats are not wired as part of the closed loop, being normally open, so separate wiring is needed back to the box.

If more than one mat is to be used they need not each be wired back separately. To avoid making connections where they may be visible, another pair of wires can be joined into the one mat joint and run off to the second one. Mats are connected in parallel, not in series as the sensors in the loop.

Other wiring

If a delay is to be used on the exit door, this sensor must be connected by a separate pair of wires back to the delay terminals on the control box. In some models there may be a wire link across the delay terminals which has to be cut if the delay is used, but left intact if it is not.

For remote setting at the exit door a separate pair of wires must be run from the key switch or lock switch back to the appropriate terminals on the control panel. As this is used as an alternative to the delay, the exit door sensor is therefore included in the loop and does not have an independent run back to control. Remote setting wire, like that of the bell, renders the system vulnerable, as any damage could inactivate the whole system. It should therefore be concealed and protected along the whole of its run.

Although useful in some circumstances, a better plan for exit doors is to use the key switch or switch lock as a shunt for the exit door sensor. This only needs to be wired across the sensor and does not need a special run back to the control box. If broken, its only effect will be that the exit door sensor is still active when the door is unlocked; thus there is no risk to security. The key or lock switch is wired so that it shorts out the sensor when the device is unlocked and is therefore wired in parallel with the sensor.

Whether used for remote setting or as a shunt, the wiring from the key switch must bridge the gap between the door and the frame. A special high-flexibility lead with or without a terminal block is made for this purpose, but is not absolutely essential. Ordinary flex will do providing it is left hanging in a short loop across the gap. Stranded wire preferably with a large number of fine strands, must be used for this, not solid conductor.

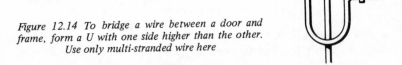

Figure 12.14 To bridge a wire between a door and frame, form a U with one side higher than the other. Use only multi-stranded wire here

Panic buttons need a run of twin wire back to the control panel. This is not particularly vulnerable as with many, in fact most, control systems the button can be cancelled by re-pressing, so it would be pointless for an intruder to attack the wiring when all he needs to do is to press the button to stop the alarm. In the case of the one commercial control unit which keeps the alarm going irrespective of what happens to the button or its wiring, the wiring is obviously unimportant once the bell has been pressed. So in either case there is no need to go to extreme lengths to protect the wiring. It can be run neatly in accord with normal practice. An exception is the case of high-risk commerical applications such as cashier's desks in banks, post offices, etc. Both button and wiring should be concealed, the button will probably be of the lockable type which needs a key to reset, so attacking the wiring is the only way the alarm could be silenced, unless of course the above mentioned control unit is used.

Window foil is used to protect non-opening glass areas, and this is terminated by small connecting blocks which can be fixed to the window frame or stuck on to the glass itself (many are self-adhesive). The foil is wired in series with the rest of the loop, so if there is a sensor protecting an adjacent opening window, the foil can conveniently be connected in series with this.

Testing

When the installation is complete, it should be tested. While many systems have silent test facilities for routine use, every part of the system after installation should be tested by actual operation. Every sensor should be operated — doors, windows and mats, (except of course the window foil!) — allowing the bell to ring each time. There is no need to let the bell ring a long time, have someone stationed at the control panel to switch off after it has rung a second or two. If two bells have been fitted, check that both are ringing. Also test the entry and exit facilities. If there are any internal bypass switches check that they are functioning by seeing whether the associated sensors are inoperative when they are closed.

After this initial test, the test facilities given on the control panel should be adequate for day-to-day checking of the system. However, an occasional bell test is advised. Most people find that they do this inadvertently, especially in the first few weeks following installation, by accidentally setting off the alarm themselves. So be particularly careful late in the evening and at night if you don't want to disturb the neighbours and have the real thing, should it occur, ignored.

It is prudent to arrange for someone living nearby, usually a neighbour, to serve as a key-holder when one is absent. In the case of commercial premises, the key-holder should be known to the local police, and if possible be someone living not very far away. Thus in the case of either a false alarm or an actual break-in, the alarm can be silenced as soon as possible and an investigation made. If the alarm is sounding for a lengthy period it may cause considerable annoyance to nearby residents, especially at night. Once the alarm has attracted attention and the intruders scared off, its work is done and it should be silenced as soon as practicable.

Some authorities recommend a device to switch off the bell after twenty minutes, and battery-operated systems would probably cease around that time due to polarisation of the batteries. Remember that cooperation from others may depend on maintaining goodwill. So, avoid false alarms if at all possible, keep bell tests short and at reasonable times, and arrange for a key-holder to silence the system with the minimum of delay in the event of an actual break-in. Make sure though that the system is re-set afterwards even if the alarm appears to be false.

13

General Security

Security, as pointed out several times before, is relative. While premises can be made more secure they cannot be made absolutely safe. However, it *is* possible to achieve a degree of security which would make a burglary highly unlikely. It is obviously wise to make the premises as secure in so far as cost and convenience will allow. The installation of a well-designed alarm system will go a long way to increasing security by deterring would-be intruders, and alarming them and neighbours should a break-in be tried.

However, reliance should not be placed solely on an alarm system, however good it may be. A building with poor physical security may tempt a burglar in spite of the alarm, in the hope of a snatching a few valuables before making a quick getaway, or even silencing the alarm. General security should therefore be as high as possible, and an alarm system regarded as an additional defence.

Front door security

The average front-door lock is one of the easiest things to open by an experienced thief. It can be sprung open by means of a thin piece of plastic slipped between the door and the frame, or if the door has glass panels, one of these can be broken and a hand slipped through to open the lock from the inside. Many locks have the staple (the part on the frame that the lock engages into) fixed by short screws into the surface of the wood. A good shoulder-charge can often loosen the screws or tear them out, levering with a jemmy can do the same.

Any conventional locks, or springlatches as they are more accurately termed, should be immediately replaced with a deadlock, that is one with a bolt that cannot be retracted without a key, and one which has at least five levers. For maximum security up to ten-lever locks can be obtained. The average springlatch has two levers and can be picked without much trouble. Another desirable feature is steel inserts inside the bolt which foil any attempt to saw through it with a hacksaw.

It is generally held that the mortice lock, i.e. one that is fitted in the door, offers greater security than the surface type which is screwed to the inside surface (*Figure 13.1*). This is because it cannot be either removed from the inside should an intruder gain entrance elsewhere and wish to establish an escape route, or burst off the door by force.

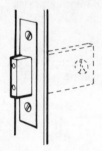

Figure 13.1 Mortice deadlock. This should be fitted only when door is thick enough to avoid weakening it when wood is excavated

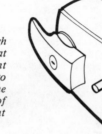

Figure 13.2 Surface deadlatch, high security type. This is fixed by screws at side and bolts through door from front keyplate, and can be double locked to prevent opening from inside without the key. This type can be fitted in place of many ordinary springlatches without modifying or cutting door

However, this needs qualification. By removing wood from a door to make the cavity necessary for fitting a mortice lock, the door is weakened at that point. Should the door be a thin one (and many modern ones are) fitting such a lock could actually create a security hazard. The application of force could splinter the wood around the lock enabling the door to be forced open. Similarly, the frame is weakened by a recessed cavity for the bolt and could likewise be damaged.

Some modern mortice locks are made especially thin to overcome this problem, but for a thin door the value of a mortice lock is very dubious. Security surface locks offer better protection in such situations. Bolts from the keyplate pass right through the door from the front to the lock on the back, and wood screws enter the door sideways through the side flange on the lock (*Figure 13.2*). Thus it is impossible to remove the lock from either side while the door is closed, and extremely unlikely that it could be burst off with force. The staple is also secured by sideways screws which are concealed when the door is closed.

One trick that has been used by intruders is to spring the door frame apart with a car jack at the point where the lock is fitted. Often it can be bowed sufficiently to disengage the lock bolt from the staple or rebate plate. To minimise this possibility, the frame should have solid support at the sides. Weak materials such as plaster should be excavated and replaced with concrete, especially near the locks on both sides of the door, and any gaps of course should be filled with the same material. Further security can be afforded by having two locks spaced apart. This adds to the inconvenience of locking and unlocking and means an extra key, and is therefore one of those situations where a decision must be made between convenience and extra security.

Bolts placed at the top and bottom of the door effectively defeat frame springing, but obviously cannot be used when the occupants are out, at least not on the exit door. They should, though be fitted for night use.

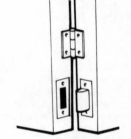

Figure 13.3 Dog (hinge) bolt. Interlocks door and frame on hinge side when door is closed. Prevents removal of door if hinge pin is removed with outward opening doors. Two should be fitted, top and bottom

Most doors swing inward, but any exterior door opening outward is vulnerable to attack to the hinges, as the hinge-body is exposed on the opening side. If the pin is removed, the door can easily be opened. To prevent this, dog or hinge bolts (*Figure 13.3*) can be fitted to the hinge side of the door and frame. These consist of a recess plate and engaging lug fitted to the door and frame. When the door is closed they interlock and prevent the door being pulled away from the frame should the hinge be damaged.

The back door

Many householders make the mistake of properly securing and locking the front door, yet having only the most rudimentary protection on the back. This is in spite of the fact that a break-in through the back of the premises is far more likely.

A good deadlock should be fitted and in addition, bolts at the top and bottom. As the back door is not usually the exit door, the bolts should be used both at night and when leaving the premises, even if only for a few minutes.

A fact that most householders find rather surprising is that locks and bolts are necessary not only to make *an entry* difficult, but also *an exit.* Should an intruder succeeed in gaining entrance by some unexpected means, one of the first things he does is to open up an escape route. This not only enables him to make a quick exit if disturbed, but also allows him to remove large and bulky articles.

Most back doors could be opened from the inside by drawing the bolts and turning the key obligingly left in the lock by the occupant; this is therefore the most favoured path. If the burglar finds that he

Figure 13.4 Mortice rackbolt, with key. This needs only a hole drilled in door or window. The window type is shorter. Another smaller hole is required to insert the key

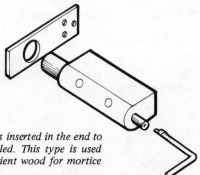

Figure 13.5 Surface rackbolt. A key is inserted in the end to operate. All fixing screws are concealed. This type is used where a door or window has insufficient wood for mortice type

cannot open any of the doors from the inside, he is virtually in a trap and is unlikely to stay very long. Certainy he will not struggle with large articles through a window or fanlight, and will have to content himself with a few smaller items.

The moral is never to leave the back-door key in the lock, and instead of the normal draw bolts, fit rack bolts, which can only be operated with a simple key. Mostly, these are of the mortice type, and as the hole required for fitting is quite small compared to that of a mortice lock, there is little weakening of the door. There are also surface units in which all the screws are concealed, some of these have the advantage that they can be shot manually without a key, although of course a key is necessary to draw them (*Figure 13.4* and *13.5*).

If any exterior door seems to be unduly flimsy, it would be a wise course to invest in a more robust one. Do not forget the frame, if this too appears weak, it could be replaced or reinforced.

Door reinforcement

In some commercial premises where high security is required, even a stout wooden door may be insufficient, so it should be reinforced by covering the outside with a sheet of mild steel of 16 gauge or thicker. The edges should be turned over and secured to the door edges by a row of wood screws.

Over the main surface, coach bolts should be fitted at intervals of not less than 9 in (225 mm) apart, the heads on the outside, and passing through the stiles and rails (the main vertical and horizontal members). On the inside, large washers should be fitted underneath the nuts over which the bolt-ends should be burred.

A good quality mortice deadlock of at least five levers should be fitted together with mortice rack bolts if the door is not to be used for final exit. The increased weight will require one or more extra hinges, and hinge bolts should also be fitted. Once again do not overlook the frame. In addition to ensuring that it is well supported at the sides, a strip of angle iron screwed to the inside of the frame at the opening side will prevent the insertion of an instrument such as a jemmy to force the door and frame apart.

Windows

The majority of entries are made through windows so these deserve special attention. Windows are often the most neglected parts of the building from the security angle, which is probably *why* most entries are made through them. Few burglars will attempt to get through a broken pane of glass, there is too great a risk of a bad cut unless all the glass is removed from the frame which would take too long.

Entries are made by opening the window by one of several means. This can be by manipulation of the catch from outside; breaking a window and operating the catch through the broken pane; removing weathered and broken putty and sliding the glass out intact; prising the window with a jemmy to release it; and entering through a window left open (this is equivalent to a 'Burglars Welcome' sign).

If then, a window can be prevented from opening and all the putty and surrounding woodwork is sound, it is reasonably secure. There are a number of devices available to prevent opening from the outside. The mortice rack bolt can be obtained in a shorter version than that used for doors. This is ideal for sash windows as it effectively locks the two windows together. Two bolts should be fitted, one on each side of the frame. Mortice bolts can also be used in a wooden framed hinged window providing there is sufficient depth of wood to accommodate it. Where there is insufficient wood a surface-mounting window bolt is also available. In the case of sash windows, the window can be left open a few inches for ventilation and locked in that position.

A cheap alternative for windows that are rarely opened is to screw the two frames together with long wood screws. This can also be done with hinged windows, passing the screw at an angle through the window frame into the surround, and should be done in at least two places. It is an excellent plan to so treat all windows unprotected by bolts when going away on holiday. Any windows that are never normally opened, and there are usually several in business premises, should be permanently screwed up in this manner.

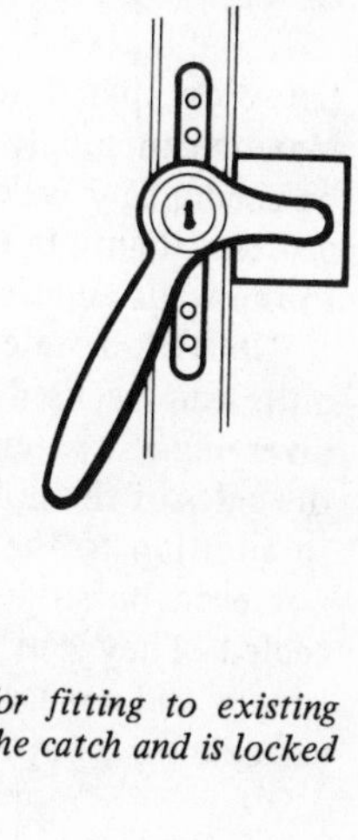

Figure 13.6 Lockable window catch. This can sometimes be fitted in place of existing window catch. A locking catch should always be specified with new windows

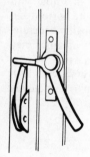

Figure 13.7 Window catch lock for fitting to existing catches. The arm swings up under the catch and is locked in place

The conventional window catch for hinged windows consisting of a pivoted handle-and-catch is available with built-in lock, and in many cases these can be used to replace the non-locking types (*Figure 13.6*). Where the catch cannot be replaced such as those welded or riveted to a metal frame, a lock can be added which holds the catch in position when closed. A similar type of lock can also be obtained for securing window-stays such as are commonly used for fanlights.

For highest security in business premises, bars should be fitted across vulnerable windows. These should be of mild steel, not less than ¾ in

(16 mm) diameter set at not more than 5 in (125 mm) apart. If over 20 in (500 mm) in length tie bars should be fitted. The ends should be buried in the stonework to a depth of at least 3 in (75 mm).

Expanded metal grilles may be visually more acceptable and when fitted to the outside gives protection against vandalism. They should be fitted to a steel frame which is grouted into the stonework.

It should be mentioned here that some d.i.y. aluminium windows are a considerable security hazard as they are screwed into the wooden surround by wood screws which are easily accessible from the outside. A few minutes work with a screwdriver and the window can be lifted out. This type of window, if fitted, can be made more secure by removing each screw, dipping the thread into a suitable liquid glue and replacing. When set, it will then be very difficult to remove the screws.

Safes

Safes less than 1 ton should be fitted to the structure of the building. Makers can supply fixing devices for recent models, and older ones can be secured by welding angle iron to the sides and top, and encasing in not less than 6 in (150 mm) of reinforced concrete which is well keyed to the walls and floor.

Underfloor safes offer better security than wall models, and smaller units can be used. They should be buried in the floor in a hole with diverging sides, reinforcement rods fitted between the safe bottom and the sides of the hole, and then the space filled with best quality concrete. In addition to the difficulty in attacking such a safe, its presence may not even be suspected by the intruder, as the top can easily be concealed. They can be supplied with a 'letterbox' facility which allows money to be placed in them by staff not having a key. This is particularly suitable for garage forecourt applications.

Other security devices

Outhouses, sheds and garages are usually protected by padlocks. Like door locks these vary in the degree of security offered. It is little use using a high quality padlock with a fitting that can simply be unscrewed from the door, or from which the hinge pin can be punched out. Locking bars should be fitted that conceal all screws when closed and have countersunk hinge pins.

Door chains are being increasingly used to prevent forced entry when opening the door to strangers, and they are excellent for this purpose. Make sure that every link is welded otherwise the joint could pull apart if forced. Choose one with enough links to enable the door to be opened sufficiently to see just who is calling. Some chains are too short and often are never used. Another useful device is the wide-angle viewer through which the occupant can see who is on the other side of the door.

As a completely darkened house during winter evenings informs everyone that the occupants are away, some householders leave a light burning in one room. If absent for any length of time though, one continuously burning light can give the game away. Electronic control units are made that switch on only during darkness, and then switch on and off in random manner. A couple of these units, one in each room wired to a table or other auxiliary lamp can give a most realistic impression of occupants in the house.

So, by achieving good general security the alarm system may never need to operate in anger, and the double defence thus established will result in peace of mind and the much needed protection to one's treasured belongings.

14

Some Typical Systems

This chapter covers some representative alarm systems. Sometimes a change of model takes place but, in general, if a manufacturer produces what he considers to be a good alarm system any radical changes are unlikely to be made for some years. It is hoped that the models described here will be available for some time to come.

There is a considerable number of products on the market, and it is not practical to try to make an exhaustive directory of all available equipment. The following is intended as a representative guide to equipment which is readily available from dealers specialising in security systems, and made by well-known makers. Equipment from small firms who sell by mail order, firms who do not supply items separately, and firms who do their own installation are not included.

Prices of individual systems have not been quoted, but some indication of cost has been included in order that meaningful comparisons can be made.

Copydex HGA 150

This system operates on a single battery, the HP 992, which is a 6 V unit. The main control is key operated. The test facility checks the loop and state of the battery only. The exit door activates the system 20 sec after switch-on, then if opened again, alarm will sound 30 sec later thus facilitating re-entry. A press-on-press-off panic button is provided.

The bell is a 6 in unit in a micro-switched steel case. An unusual feature is the small red lamp in the base of the case which comes on when the alarm is sounded. Where several houses in close proximity may have alarm systems, this identifies the source of the sound. However, being powered from a 6 V battery, the light is an additional drain and may not be bright enough if there is street lighting around.

Another unusual feature, is the provision of an internal bell in addition to the outside bell. This is a good idea but is mounted on the control box, so drawing attention to its whereabouts. A concealed box makes for maximum security.

The kit includes two pressure mats, five surface-mounting reed switches and magnets, panic button, wire, staples and fixing wall-plugs.

Eagle AB 160M

The control unit is mains operated with self-charging standby battery. It contains an internal buzzer for alarm or testing. The external bell circuit can be switched off. Thus the system can be tested without sounding the bell by means of the buzzer, although of course the bell itself would not be checked. In addition to the buzzer sounding, a light on the control box comes on when the alarm is triggered.

The alarm will sound for up to a minute, or can be set to sound continuously. Power consumption is 3 W on standby, (250 mA from 12 V battery), and 8 W on alarm. Standby current is high, and even though batteries are self-charging, a prolonged mains failure could soon discharge them. A bell, the ABA 95, is available separately. This is a 6 in open unit which takes 200 mA, and gives a sound output of 83 dB at 3 m. Mats, reed switches and other items are also available individually. It may be thought that the cost of a complete system is high considering the limited facilities.

Gents Model 61

The control unit is mains operated with battery standby, the batteries being four large special 1.5 V cells giving a total of 6 V. It is relay triggered, and the loop current is rather high, maximum loop resistance being 70 Ω. The test facility checks loop continuity only.

A feature of this system is the panic circuit which uses ordinary bell pushes but which keep the alarm sounding once the push has been pressed, thus offering maximum security.

The exit delay is from 1-4 min from the time of switching on. The alarm sounds on re-entry though, unless a bypass switch is installed, in which case it could also be used for the exit without need of the delay. The bell is a 6 in unit with an outside striker, and is housed in a fibreglass box. It takes 120 mA and delivers 88 dB. The kit includes six microswitches, with delay setting and reminder lamps which indicate when the delay exit time has expired.

This is a well-tried system that has been little changed over the years but is rather dated by the type of bell and batteries used, also the microswitches.

Newman Controls

All items of this system are sold separately — a sensible arrangement. The control unit is mains operated with battery standby. The use of an expensive battery for this purpose has been avoided by the use of a PP9, but the capacity of this battery is limited, and a maximum of 24 hours standby is quoted.

The testing facility checks loop and battery, and a panic button circuit is provided which requires the usual press-on-press-off button. Simple controls avoid the use of keys. It is in the medium price range.

Selmar

This is a basic low-cost kit, one of the least expensive complete systems available. The control unit is mains operated with battery standby, the batteries being three AD28 s. It is relay controlled, and the loop current is 60 mA. The test facility checks loop continuity only. There is a provision for a remote-setting switch and panic button which must be of the press-on-press-off type. Control is key operated.

The bell is a 6 in unit which is housed in a steel case, current is 300 mA. The main drawback is high loop current and an expensive set of batteries.

The kit includes five magnetic reed switches, two pressure mats, wire, staples and fixing materials.

Sesco Homeguard 71 Mk II

Sesco supply a wide range of security equipment of all types, but this is the popular domestic kit, it is another example of a basic low-cost outfit.

The control unit runs from the mains with standby battery which is a 12 V HP 1. It is relay operated with the usual high current associated with this type of circuit. There is a key-operated control which selects 'off', 'test', 'day' and 'night' alert. The test position checks loop continuity and the day setting is for the panic-button circuit. This means that the panic-button will only operate in the 'day' position, and not when the system is switched off.

The bell is a 6 in unit which is housed in a weatherproof cover. The kit includes six magnetic reed switches, wire and fixing materials, but no pressure mats.

Sure-guard

A considerable amount of thought and design ingenuity has evidently gone into this system, because most of the snags encountered with most others seem to have been overcome. The 'Microdrain' loop passes an incredibly low 0.1 mA which enables the system to be run on two lantern type batteries, no mains being required. Thus there are no problems with mains wiring and power cuts. The batteries, which it is claimed will last at least a year, are readily obtainable and when removed in the interests of security can be used up in a lantern torch.

The 'Completest' test facility is the most comprehensive in any domestic system. It tests not only the loop but also the control unit, and uniquely, it tests the vulnerable bell circuit all in one operation without sounding the bells. Two identical weatherproof 6-in bells are provided, one for internal and the other for external fitting (or both can be fitted outside, one at the front and the other at the back). Each gives a healthy 86 dB at 3 m at a consumption of 95 mA. Thus both bells consume less battery current than most single ones in other systems, but make a lot more noise.

There is a fuse in the control unit for the internal bell. If the wiring to this, being the most accessible, is tampered with, the fuse blows so protecting the power supply to the external bell which continues to ring.

A panic circuit, (termed 'Everlert'), will function with the system switched off, as in fact do other models, but ordinary bell pushes can be used, as once pressed nothing can stop the alarm, not even cutting the press-button wire. The system can be silenced only by pressing a concealed, unmarked 'cancel' button. Thus special latching buttons with their dubious security value are unnecessary.

The main control is a three-way lever switch giving 'test', 'off' and 'on', spring biassed so that it cannot be left in the test position. There is also a test button and an unmarked 'cancel' button which must be depressed when the control is turned 'off' otherwise the alarm will continue ringing. This gives extra security as no switch-key is used.

There is an exit delay of eight seconds which starts from the time the exit door is opened. This gives adequate time to make a normal exit through the door, but if it is not closed within the eight seconds, the alarm will sound. Once the door is closed, another eight seconds will elapse before the alarm will ring on re-opening. Thus a re-entry can be made without sounding the alarm, providing the door is shut immediately.

A remote control facility is included for which a lockswitch must be fitted to the exit door, and a buzzer wired nearby. Locking the door sets the alarm, and a short 'bleep' from the buzzer confirms that the alarm is on and set. If a window or door has been left open the buzzer sounds continuously. The bells only sound if a sensor is operated *after* the system is switched on, if already open, the buzzer sounds. This avoids false alarms when locking premises and is ideal for halls and clubrooms where there may be forgetful keyholders.

Another facility is that of mains switching. Up to 1000 W can be switched on by the alarm circuit if required. Thus lamps, floodlights, recorder, amplifier or mains siren can be activated. A 'mains activate' switch enables these devices to be switched off or on as desired, when testing the alarm circuit.

A further feature rarely found on domestic and small alarms is auto-dialling facilities. Provision is made for the connection of an auto-dialling machine or any other device requiring a normally closed pair of contacts that open when the alarm is triggered. This, together with the mains switching, operates from the panic buttons with the system switched off, as well as in the normal mode with the main alarm circuit on. A further feature which some other systems would do well to copy is that it is fully suppressed against false alarms caused by mobile radio transmissions.

So, this is quite a remarkable system, and although not the cheapest, neither is it the most expensive. The kit consists of the control unit and two bells, sensors can be obtained separately according to requirements; Sure-guard anticipate bringing out a sensor kit in the future, and also there is a possibility of a junior version having a single bell and without the mains switching and remote control facilities.

Yale

Another basically simple system runs from the mains with battery standby which consists of eight HP2 unit cells. This is a rather novel idea for an alarm system and it has the attraction of being readily obtainable and inexpensive. Experience with torches and recorders though has shown that a number of unit cells in press contact can suffer from oxidisation of terminals giving poor or intermittent contact, especially if unused for some time.

Loop current is 20 mA which gives 80 hours standby from the batteries. This is better than some, but is still rather limited. The main control is key operated, and the testing facility checks the loop, while the panic button circuit requires the press-on-press-off type. The bell is a 6 in unit in a steel case, and the kit includes five magnetic switches, two pressure mats, a key-operated remote or bypass switch (an unusual inclusion), and wire and fixing materials. A medium price outfit.

Conclusion

From this short survey it can be seen that there is a variety of systems available. Prices tend to vary, even between systems offering similar facilities. Many of the differences are of detail only. Most of these described are obtainable through security dealers also and other outlets. Some systems are available through importers in countries outside the UK or by special order direct from the makers. The names and addresses of the manufacturers are as follows:

Copydex. Copydex Ltd, 1 Torquay St, London W2 5EL.
Eagle. Eagle International, Heather Park Drive, Wembley, HAO 1SU.
Gents. Chloride Gent Ltd, Faraday Works, Leicester LE5 4JF.
Newman. Newman Controls Ltd, Unit 5, Trading Estate, Bath Rd, Bristol.
Selmar. Stellar Components Ltd, The Causeway, Maldon, Essex.
Sesco. Sesco Security Ltd, Jubilee Works, Chapel Rd, Hounslow.
Sure-Guard. Suretron Systems (UK) Ltd, Piccadilly Place, London Rd, Bath.
Yale. Yale Security Products, Wood St, Willenhall, Staffs.

15

Official Recommendations

Certain official bodies have produced recommendations regarding the construction, installation and servicing of intruder alarm systems. These mostly apply to larger systems as used in industry and in particular lay down certain standards which should be followed by commercial installers contracting to install alarm equipment on client's premises. Most of the recommendations are to be found in the British Standard, BS 4737, in its various parts. Similar IEC standards are in operation in Europe.

British Standard recommendations

For control units it is recommended that the system be key operated either by a normal key or magnetic or other coded device. As stated in an earlier chapter, this is certainly desirable for industrial premises, although not so for domestic ones.

The main exit and entrance paths should be controlled by time control, time delay, shunt lock or key switch so that it is not necessary to sound the alarm when authorised personnel enter or leave. For automatic dialling equipment, resetting should be non automatic.

The system should respond to alarm signals greater than 800 mS in duration but not to those less than 200 mS. This avoids false alarms from transient pulses picked up on the loop. Housing of the control unit should be in a mild steel case of not less than 1.2 mm thickness or material of equivalent strength, and protected by an anti-tamper micro-switch. This applies to any ancilliary equipment such as standby batteries. Here again this is not so important with domestic units where concealment is the best protection.

Standby power should be greater than for 8 hours normal operation. Here the specification seems rather lax, as mentioned previously a power failure could easily exceed this. The primary supply on the other hand should be sufficient for 4 hours alarm sounding, which seems stringent as few batteries could give this continuously if powering the bell as well, but the recommendation is for a self-powered bell. High capacity is desirable in case there may be several alarms in quick succession. There would though be at least some time between them to allow a primary battery to rest and depolarise.

According to the specification batteries should be replaced after no longer than 75% of their normal shelf life. This is a good practice for standby batteries where they probably are never actually used, but for battery systems that keep batteries active with a small drain, they will last much longer than this. It is further recommended that some indication be given by the system if battery voltage falls below that required to operate the alarm. The date of fitting should be marked on the batteries and they should function over the temperature range $-10°C$ to $+40°C$. Voltage in the system should not exceed 50 V.

As to the bell or other warning device, this should be of more than one component note, either continuous or intermittent, 1 sec on and 1 sec off. Sound level should be not less than 70 dBA mean from all directions and not less than 65 dBA in any direction at 3 m, (measuring conditions are specified in the standard). This is somewhat lower than is really desirable. The bell should be mounted in a steel box of similar strength to the control unit, and fitted with an anti-tamper switch.

Any time-limiting device to stop the bell should be automatically reset when the controls are reset. Each bell should have its own internal power supply which, if a primary cell, should be sufficient for at least 2 hours sounding, or if a rechargeable unit, enough for not less than 30 min sounding between charges. The bell should sound if signalled, if the leads are either open or short-circuited, or tested. It should not operate during opening or closing procedures. The advantages and disadvantages of self-powered bells as recommended here have already been dealt with. Bells should operate over the temperature range of $-10°C$ to $+50°C$, and with humidities between 10% – 95%.

The wiring should be a double-pole closed loop which triggeres the alarm if adjacent conductors are short circuited or any conductor is open circuited. It should be secured at intervals of not more than 500 mm apart. Flexible leads for bridging door hinges should be of annealed copper eleven strands or more each 0.2 mm diameter, p.v.c. covered insulation of not less than 0.25 mm thickness. Alternatively tinsel wire of cadmium copper tape can be utilized.

Sensor switches should operate before the door or window opens 100 mm, and all open-circuit switches must be hermetically sealed. Ceiling break-wires should be of hard-drawn copper wire 0.3-0.4 mm, fixed at intervals of not more than 600 mm with spacing between adjacent wires being less than 100 mm. If fitted in rods or tubes these should be not more than 1 m long.

Window foil must be less than 0.04 mm thick and less than 12.5 mm wide. It should not be carried across cracks or butt joints and on un-framed glass the take-off connectors should not be more than 100 mm from the glass edge. Recommended configuration is a strip around all four edges of the glass panel, 50-100 mm from the edge, along the middle of the glass if it is no more than 600 mm in height; or parallel strips no more than 200 mm apart; or on unframed glass a loop of 200 mm apart. It is further stipulated that the foils should be part of a double pole circuit.

Length of alarm time

Another body, the British Security Industry Association has a recommen-dation regarding the time that an alarm be allowed to sound after being triggered. The suggestion is that a cut-out be fitted which stops the alarm after 20 minutes, this being considered a reasonable time for it to have accomplished its purpose.

Conclusion

These recommendations are a guide to good practice for installers for the larger commercial systems. Few if any domestic and small business systems comply with all the standards, in fact some as we have discussed earlier would be a disadvantage in the different circumstances.

There is a National Supervisory Council for Intruder Alarms whose primary function is to enforce the British Standards. This body has an approved roll of installation firms who accept the Standards and guarantee that all work done by them will comply with them.

The British Standard also covers servicing and maintenance pro-cedures, and it is recommended that professional installation firms consult these.

Index